purely golden door

purely golden door

essential recipes

for health and vitality

from

The Golden Door Health Retreats

MURDOCH BOOKS

contents

nutrition, exercise, relaxation

The Golden Door is more than a place: it's a style of living that encompasses products, services and facilities specifically designed to create a healthy mind, body and spirit.

Nutrition, exercise and relaxation are the cornerstones of The Golden Door philosophy and these, combined, deliver a holistic approach to health and wellbeing. In our two retreats we teach the art of skilful living and graceful ageing and we also acknowledge that the goal of a healthy mind, body and spirit continues outside our facilities. This is the inspiration behind *Purely Golden Door*.

Purely Golden Door includes a collection of favourite dishes from our Queensland health retreat, together with a range of great new recipes developed by our talented Executive Chefs from both retreats. The nutritional information provided for each recipe allows you to monitor more carefully the amount of fat and the number of calories in each dish you prepare.

At The Golden Door we believe that a healthy balanced diet leads to enhanced wellbeing and vitality. It can boost your immunity and even ward off some diseases. A healthy balanced diet is one that is low in saturated (and trans) fats, rich in nutritious carbohydrates, high in fibre and contains a wide range of foods to meet vitamin and mineral requirements. The meals we serve at our health retreats, and which we are delighted to present to you here, allow you to follow these recommendations for the rest of your life.

Purely Golden Door is part of our ongoing commitment to your improved health and we hope you enjoy using it.

Brook Ramage
National General Manager

why Golden Door?

The Golden Door Program is an organized live-in experience that encompasses exercise sessions with trained professionals, a specially designed low-fat menu of delicious spa cuisine, holistic therapies and spa treatments, and sessions with physical educators and nutrition advisors.

Much of the Program is focused on giving you the educational and experiential tools you need to make long-lasting changes to your lifestyle. The *Purely Golden Door* cookbook is one of these tools and provides a great selection of spa cuisine recipes that can be easily created at home every day.

The Golden Door Program food is prepared as part of a regime of exercise, education, wellbeing and nutrition. During one of our Programs, guests adhere to guidelines such as seafood served on average four times a week and dessert served only once.

However, at The Golden Door Health Retreat – Elysia independent guests can enjoy a greater variety of foods than Progam guests. During an independent stay, guests will have a daily choice of lean red meat, chicken, seafood or vegetarian cuisine, with eggs, dessert and juices offered each day.

detoxification

The Golden Door Program focuses on detoxifying the body. Every day your body is bombarded by toxins. These might be in the environment (pollution, cigarette smoke); in your food (naturally-occurring food toxins, chemical additives or the chemicals used in growing our food); medications; alcohol, caffeine and other drugs; or the toxins produced in the body in normal metabolic processes and those produced in response to exposure to UV and other types of radiation, to excessive exercise and even over-eating.

Detoxification is a normal bodily process, however, wellbeing and good health depend on your body's detox systems working properly. To minimize the chances of your system being over-worked, you need to make good lifestyle and food choices.

At The Golden Door we believe that the key to effective detoxification involves just two things: taking the burden off your body (by removing as many of the toxins as possible) and providing your body with all the nutrients it needs.

To reduce the burden on your detox system we suggest that you:
• Don't smoke;
• Manage your stress and make time for relaxation;
• Minimize your exposure to UV radiation;
• Minimize the use of potentially harmful chemicals, including household cleaning products and garden chemicals (there are safer, more natural and environmentally-friendly alternatives to many pesticides and herbicides);
• Buy organically-grown produce when possible and wash all your fruit and vegetables thoroughly;
• Don't over-eat;
• Exercise regularly but not excessively;
• Limit your consumption of caffeine, alcohol and other unnecessary drugs.

To maximize the nutrients you need for effective detoxification we suggest that you:
• Focus on plant foods — vegetables, fruit, legumes and whole grains. Plant foods are superfoods when it comes to detoxification. They are rich in vitamins, minerals and phytochemicals (plant

nutrients). It is important not only to eat a large quantity but also the widest possible variety. Certain plant foods have been found to be particularly rich in compounds that boost your body's detoxification capabilities. These include blueberries, strawberries, blackcurrants, boysenberries, raspberries, red grapes, apples, citrus fruits, watermelon, alfalfa sprouts, watercress, broccoli, cauliflower, carrots, sweet potato, pumpkin, tomatoes, spinach, garlic, ginger, onion, all types of legumes, all types of whole grains, spices such as chilli, cinnamon and paprika and the herbs, rosemary, coriander and sage;

- Ensure you get essential omega-6 and omega-3 fatty acids by eating twice-weekly servings of oily fish and small portions of unsalted nuts and seeds each day;
- Include small servings of lean, preferably organically-reared, red meat for zinc and iron;
- Avoid, or keep to an absolute minimum, foods that are largely devoid of nutrients, such as processed cereal products (like white bread, pasta and rice), sugar and sugary foods (cakes, biscuits, soft drink and cordials);
- Reduce your salt intake. Instead of salt and salty sauces, flavour your food with herbs and spices, which are rich in phytochemicals;
- Drink at least 2 litres (70 fl oz/8 cups) of water each day.

our nutrition philosophy

At The Golden Door, we believe that food is one of life's greatest sources of pleasure. We also believe that eating the right kinds of foods and preparing them in the healthiest possible way is essential to wellbeing. In our hectic lives, it can be all too easy to rely on heavily processed, 'convenience' foods, which are often nutrient-poor, calorie-dense and loaded with unhealthy fats, added sugars and salt.

We recommend getting back to basics by eating more food in the state nature intended and limiting the fats, added sugar and salt in our diets. Healthy eating is about eating fresh, minimally processed foods: plenty of colourful vegetables and fruit, a variety of whole grains and legumes and small servings of nuts, seeds and (for non-vegetarians) fish and lean meat. Eating the widest possible variety of foods over the course of a week is the best way to ensure that your body gets all the essential nutrients it needs for optimal health.

Our recipes are delicious and simple to prepare and have been created with health and nutrition in mind. Our chefs play a critical role in the development of our spa cuisine. They have had to adapt their cooking styles and recipe development to minimize the use of, and sometimes even exclude, ingredients such as salt, oil, butter, sugar and cream to develop well-balanced recipes.

While the ingredients in each dish play a key role, our cooking methods will also ensure you retain the greatest amount of nutrients in your food and reduce the need to add a lot of salt and fat for flavour. If there is a particular ingredient that you don't like or can't eat, simply replace it with an alternative flavour or spice. Allowances are made for those with special requirements or intolerances.

the nutritional information in our recipes

Each recipe is accompanied by nutritional information on the energy, protein, fat, carbohydrate, fibre and sodium provided by each serving. This information will help you determine which meals and snacks best meet your needs and whether you should reduce or increase the portion we suggest. As a guide, the size of our servings is appropriate for a moderately active person.

kilojoules for energy

The energy value of food is determined by how much protein, carbohydrate and fat is in that food. Protein and carbohydrate provide roughly the same amount of energy (16 kJ or 4 Cals per gram), while fat provides over double that amount (36 kJ or 9 Cals per gram).

Body fat loss depends on consuming less energy than you burn — in other words, reducing the added fats and sugars in your meals and trimming down your portions, while increasing the amount of exercise you do.

protein for satisfaction

Protein is vital to the health of your hormone and immune systems as well as for the repair and growth of every tissue in your body. Most people need 1–2 grams per day for each kilogram of their weight.

Animal sources of protein (meat, fish, eggs and dairy foods) are considered to provide 'complete protein' as they contain all the essential amino acids your body needs. Plant protein sources (legumes, nuts, seeds and whole grains) are 'incomplete proteins' because, in most cases, they contain all but one or two of the essential amino acids. This is why it is important in vegetarian meal planning to incorporate a wide variety of protein sources to avoid amino acid deficiency. More specifically, if you combine legumes with grains, or legumes with nuts or seeds you will have a complete complement of essential amino acids.

Protein takes longer to digest and absorb than carbohydrate or fat, making protein-rich foods relatively filling. So the most satisfying meals tend to be those that contain both unprocessed carbohydrate-rich and protein-rich foods. These meals can help to prevent sudden dips in blood glucose (hypoglycaemia) by keeping the levels more stable.

carbohydrates for fuel

Carbohydrates (as starch) are found in grains, legumes and vegetables and (as sugars) in fruit and milk. As a group of foods, they are an important source of fibre, phytochemicals, minerals, vitamins and, most importantly, energy. Carbohydrates are broken down into glucose, which is your body's preferred fuel. Your body's stores of carbohydrate — the glucose in your blood and the glycogen in your muscles and liver — must be refilled during the day. When carbohydrate stores run low you feel tired, lethargic and will be unable to concentrate.

Eating carbohydrates at regular intervals throughout the day will keep your energy levels up. It is important to include nutritious types of carbohydrate: whole grains and cereals (such as muesli and porridge, grainy breads, wholemeal pasta, brown rice, quinoa); starchy vegetables (like sweet potato and parsnip); fruit and legumes; and milk and yoghurt (and soy- or rice-based alternatives). Because they contain few nutrients (besides carbohydrates), your intake of processed carbohydrate foods (white rice, white bread, white flour etc) and added sugars should be limited.

The more active you are, the more carbohydrates you need to eat. About 150–250 grams of carbohydrate per day is needed by a person who participates in light to moderate exercise. Very active people can often require in excess of 350–400 grams per day.

In recent years high-protein diets that are very low in carbohydrates have become increasingly popular for weight loss. These diets fail to differentiate between nutritious carbohydrate foods that are essential to good health and those that are highly processed and/or high in added sugars. Many of these diets pose a possible long-term danger to your health, particularly those that recommend less than 100 grams of carbohydrate per day, leading to a potentially harmful condition called ketosis.

the glycaemic index

The glycaemic index (GI) is a ranking of carbohydrate foods based on the effect they have on blood glucose levels. Foods that are digested and absorbed more slowly cause a gradual rise in glucose in the blood. These foods have a lower GI ranking than foods that cause a rapid rise in blood glucose levels.

There are a number of reasons why it is desirable to choose carbohydrate foods with a low GI:

- They keep your blood glucose levels stable and so prevent hypoglycaemia (and its associated sugar-cravings);
- They keep you feeling satisfied for longer;
- To break them down requires less insulin (a hormone that tells your body to store fat) and so they can help prevent the gaining of body fat.

Carbohydrate foods with a low GI include: grainy and sourdough breads; wholegrain breakfast cereals (like muesli and oat porridge); wheat pasta; barley; milk; yoghurt; most kinds of fruit; all kinds of legumes and nuts; sweet potato; basmati rice; sweet corn and peas.

High GI foods include: white and wholemeal bread, processed breakfast cereals like cornflakes; over-ripe fruit, dates and watermelon; white potato; most white and brown rice varieties.

fats for vitality

Because fat provides double the energy of either carbohydrate or protein, it is far easier to over-consume kilojoules and gain weight if you regularly choose foods that are high in fat.

It is recommended that roughly 30 per cent of your total energy intake comes from fat. This translates to around 50–60 grams of fat per day for someone who is not particularly active or wants to reduce body fat levels. More active people require 80–100 grams of fat per day.

More important than how much fat you eat, however, is the type of fat (or fatty acids) you eat. Certain fatty acids are essential to good health. Others are potentially damaging to health.

the healthy fats. Omega-3 fatty acids and some of the omega-6 fatty acids (polyunsaturated fats) are known as essential fatty acids, being vital to the health of every cell in your body.

Omega-3s are found in oily fish (such as salmon, trout, tuna, sardines and mackerel), linseeds (flaxseeds), walnuts and pecans. Omega-6 fatty acids are found in nuts and seeds and the oils derived from them.

The monounsaturated fatty acids in extra virgin olive oil, avocado, nuts and seeds come packed with antioxidants and vitamins and can help lower cholesterol levels.

the unhealthy fats. Saturated fatty and trans fatty acids are the two types of fat you should limit.

Saturated fatty acids are found in the fat on meat and poultry, full-cream milk and yoghurt, cream, cheese and butter and in commercial cakes, biscuits and pastries. These can raise blood cholesterol levels. Trans fatty acids are found naturally in the fat in dairy products (and in products from other ruminants). Processed foods, however, are by far the biggest contributors in most people's diets.

To ensure a healthy balance of fatty acids, eat oily fish at least twice a week, have a small portion of unsalted nuts and seeds each day and minimize the amount of oil you use in cooking and dressings.

fibre for cleansing

Fibre is the indigestible carbohydrate in plant-based foods. Eating enough fibre is important to prevent constipation and the build up of toxins. Fibre can help regulate blood glucose levels, reduce cholesterol levels and the risk of heart disease, reduce the risk of bowel cancer and help with weight management. It is recommended that you consume 30–40 grams of fibre each day from a variety of sources, including whole grains, legumes, fruits, vegetables, nuts and seeds.

sodium for life

Your body requires only 200–800 milligrams of sodium per day. This is far less than the Australian average intake of close to 5000 milligrams per day. You can reduce your consumption of sodium by reducing the amount of salt you add to food. We like to use the minimum amount of salt in our cooking but small amounts of seasoning are essential to enhance the flavour of most food. We recommend that you use sea salt. Please note that additional seasoning with a small pinch of salt and pepper is not included in the nutritional analysis given for each recipe.

For most of us, it is the sodium in processed food products that is the biggest contributor to a high sodium intake. Sodium can come in many guises, as plain old salt (standard table salt, sea salt, Celtic salt or rock salt), as the flavour enhancer monosodium glutamate (MSG), and as baking powder (sodium bicarbonate).

At The Golden Door, we aim to keep total sodium intake to below 2300 milligrams per day, in line with current population recommendations.

adjusting the recipes for those with special requirements

The Golden Door Health Retreats cater for guests with food intolerances and allergies and a number of the recipes included in this book can be adjusted for gluten-, wheat- and lactose-free diets.

gluten-free diets. Some people have a sensitivity to gluten, a protein found in a number of grains, including barley, oats, rye, triticale and wheat, and all the products and flours made from these.

Gluten-free alternatives include the following (and the products and flours derived from them): amaranth; arrowroot, buckwheat; chickpeas; corn; lentils; quinoa; rice; sago; soy; and tapioca. These can be substituted when gluten-containing grains or products are used in any of our recipes.

When we suggest wheat (including spelt) flour, you can substitute the following gluten-free flour: sift together equal parts soy flour, corn flour (pure corn flour, not wheaten) and rice flour.

A gluten-free baking powder can be made by mixing 2 tablespoons cream of tartar with 1 tablespoon sodium bicarbonate. Add 2 teaspoons of this to each cup of gluten-free flour mix. We have found that xanthan gum improves the texture of gluten-free baked products. Just add 1 or 2 teaspoons to our muffin recipes.

wheat-free diets. An increasing number of people report feeling better when they avoid wheat-containing foods. The following contain wheat: regular breads, biscuits, cakes, flours, batter and pasta; couscous; semolina; wheat bran; wheat meal. As long as wheat is replaced by alternative grain foods (such as barley, buckwheat, quinoa, rice or rye) there is no reason why a wheat-free diet should not be nutritionally complete. There are also specialized wheat-free products now available from health food shops and good supermarkets, including wheat-free pastas and breads.

lactose-free diets. Some people have trouble digesting lactose, a sugar found in dairy milk. Most people with lactose intolerance are able to consume a small amount without difficulty. Yoghurt is much lower in lactose than milk and is often better tolerated. An increasing number of adults are also recognising that the protein in cow's milk (specifically casein) is the basis of their food sensitivity. Calcium-fortified soy milk is a milk substitute as is rice milk (although it contains less protein than cow's and soy milk). Choose a soy milk made from whole soy beans.

In some of our recipes we recommend a malt-free soy milk, as malt unnecessarily increases the carbohydrate content of soy milk. It is also an appropriate choice for people with both a gluten intolerance and a lactose/dairy protein intolerance.

the importance of exercise

Your body is designed to move. Sensible, moderate exercise strengthens your immune system and has been shown to lower the risk of depression, stress, headaches, various cancers and cardiovascular disease. Excessive and infrequent exercise on the other hand actually increases the oxidative stress on your body and can deplete your immune system.

Regular, moderate exercise is a key component of The Golden Door philosophy, not only for healthy weight maintenance and to help lose body fat, but also for the numerous health benefits it offers:
• Exercise causes your body to release happy chemicals called endorphins, which help to relieve tension and stress;
• Exercise strengthens and builds muscle. Because muscle is a metabolically active tissue, the more muscle you have the more energy you burn, even when you are not exercising;
• Regular exercise causes your body to adapt to burning more fat while you are at rest (in preference to carbohydrate which it wants to save for exercise). It also increases your muscles' storage of glucose as glycogen so that you can burn more energy during work-outs;
• When you raise your heart rate during exercise, you are helping to improve the health of your cardiovascular system. The critical processes of detoxification and cell renewal are supported by regular exercise because blood (and the essential nutrients and oxygen it carries) is pumped around your body more effectively. The result is boosted immunity and even a reduced risk of some diseases;
• Our lymphatic system is a vital component of our immune system. Blood is pumped around the body by the heart, but to move lymphatic fluid around the body we rely on movement and the contraction of our muscles. Nothing contracts the muscles better than exercise.

relaxation

At The Golden Door we recognize the complex variations in people's lives and the importance of balance. Relaxation offers clarity to the mind and renews energy in the body. At our health retreats we strongly recommend the need to balance, rejuvenate and invigorate the body and mind through any number of relaxation techniques. The methods people use to relax are as different as their lives — some use exercise, meditation, a hobby or quietly preparing a meal at the end of a busy day. The essence of relaxation is not how we relax our bodies but how we clear our minds, and its importance in our general health should not be underestimated. We believe that with the right nutrition, exercise and relaxation practices, good health can be sustained for the rest of your life.

dawn

dawn

Sunrise is one of the most beautiful times of the day but many of us miss it in the hustle and bustle of our busy lives. If you can, take the time to wake up slowly, stretching your body and acclimatizing it to a new day. Our green drink of citrus juices sweetened with a little honey is a gentle and cleansing way to start your morning. And for winter dawns when you're feeling a little under the weather, the cold and flu tea with citrus and ginger will help to revitalize your system.

Juices and smoothies made with colourful fruits and vegetables are packed with health benefits as well as being quick and convenient to whip up in the morning. Drinking a juice a day is such an easy way to boost your fruit intake and give your body a hefty dose of protective plant nutrients.

fresh vitality pure nourishing luscious healthy balance variety fresh vitality pure nourishing luscious healthy balance variety

cold and flu tea

3 garlic cloves
5 cm (2 inch) piece of fresh ginger
1 cinnamon stick
juice of 4 lemons
2 ginger tea bags
1 tablespoon honey

Bring 2 litres (70 fl oz/8 cups) of water to the boil in a pan. Finely chop the garlic, ginger and cinnamon in a food processor and then add to the boiling water.

Add the lemon juice, ginger tea bags and honey. Boil for 5 minutes and then strain before serving.

Note: If the tea is too strong for your taste, you can add more water.

Makes 2 litres (70 fl oz/8 cups)

Nutrition per cup: Energy: 77 kJ (18 Cals); Protein: 0 g;
Total fat: 0 g; Carbohydrate: 4 g; Fibre: 0 g; Sodium: 1 mg

the green drink

juice of 2 oranges
juice of 1 lemon
handful of fresh parsley
1 garlic clove, chopped
small piece of ginger, peeled and chopped
pinch of chilli (optional)
1 teaspoon honey

Mix all the ingredients in a blender, serve immediately and get healthy!

Serves 1

Nutrition per serve: Energy: 407 kJ (97 Cals); Protein: 2 g;
Total fat: 0.4 g; Carbohydrate: 20 g; Fibre: 2 g; Sodium: 28 mg

mixed berry smoothie

150 g (5½ oz/1 cup) mixed berries (fresh or frozen)
125 g (4½ oz/½ cup) low-fat yoghurt
½ cup ice

Put all the ingredients in a blender and mix for 2 minutes.

Serves 1

Nutrition per serve: Energy: 413 kJ (99 Cals); Protein: 10 g;
Total fat: 0.4 g; Carbohydrate: 12 g; Fibre: 4 g; Sodium: 97 mg

banana smoothie

115 g (4 oz/½ cup) mashed ripe banana
125 ml (4 fl oz/½ cup) skim milk
125 g (4½ oz/½ cup) low-fat yoghurt
1 cup ice
1 tablespoon LSA (linseed, sunflower and almond blend)

Put all the ingredients in a blender and mix for 2 minutes.

Serves 1

Nutrition per serve: Energy: 1169 kJ (279 Cals); Protein: 17 g;
Total fat: 6 g; Carbohydrate: 38 g; Fibre: 4 g; Sodium: 147 mg

melon wheatgerm smoothie

1 cup rock melon chunks
1 cup ice
125 g (4½ oz/½ cup) low-fat yoghurt
1 tablespoon wheatgerm

Put all the ingredients in a blender and mix for 2 minutes.

Serves 1

Nutrition per serve: Energy: 521 kJ (124 Cals); Protein: 10 g;
Total fat: 1 g; Carbohydrate: 18 g; Fibre: 3 g; Sodium: 109 mg

melon, apple and spirulina juice

½ cup honeydew melon chunks
½ cup pineapple pieces
1 green apple
1 teaspoon spirulina powder

Juice all the fruit and blend with the powder. Serve immediately.

Serves 1

Nutrition per serve: Energy: 547 kJ (131 Cals); Protein: 3 g; Total fat: 0.5 g; Carbohydrate: 30 g; Fibre: 6 g; Sodium: 62 mg

mango, mint and pear frappé

2 pears, unpeeled
2 teaspoons chopped fresh mint
1 small mango, peeled
1 cup ice

Juice the pears and then mix in a blender with the remaining ingredients.

Serves 1

Nutrition per serve: Energy: 1079 kJ (258 Cals); Protein: 3 g; Total fat: 0.6 g; Carbohydrate: 51 g; Fibre: 10 g; Sodium: 9 mg

apple, orange, celery and ginger juice

2 green apples
1 orange
1 celery stalk
1 teaspoon grated fresh ginger

Put all the ingredients through a juicer and stir together before serving.

Serves 1

Nutrition per serve: Energy: 807 kJ (193 Cals); Protein: 3 g; Total fat: 0.5 g; Carbohydrate: 44 g; Fibre: 4 g; Sodium: 41 mg

iron drink

50 g (1¾ oz) fresh parsley
1 teaspoon spirulina powder
250 ml (9 fl oz/1 cup) freshly squeezed orange juice
25 g (1 oz) baby spinach

Blend all the ingredients together until smooth. Chill before serving.

Serves 1

Nutrition per serve: Energy: 398 kJ (95 Cals); Protein: 4 g; Total fat: 0.5 g; Carbohydrate: 20 g; Fibre: 4 g; Sodium: 63 mg

protein drink

1 tablespoon chopped cashew nuts
1 ripe banana
250 ml (9 fl oz/1 cup) skim milk
1 teaspoon honey (optional)
1 tablespoon protein powder

Mix together all the ingredients in a blender. Serve immediately.

Serves 1 (makes 500 ml/2 cups)

CHEF'S TIP: If you don't have any protein powder, use 4 egg whites instead.

Nutrition per serve: Energy: 1293 kJ (309 Cals); Protein: 26 g; Total fat: 7 g; Carbohydrate: 36 g; Fibre: 3 g; Sodium: 252 mg

morning

morning

Starting the day with a well-balanced, nutritious breakfast will energize you and leave you better able to concentrate throughout the morning. For people who want to lose weight, eating breakfast is one of the simplest ways to prevent over-eating later in the day. Keep breakfast interesting by not always having the same thing.

The ideal breakfast contains carbohydrates to help you refuel after your overnight fast. Low GI (glycaemic index) carbohydrates like fruit, muesli, porridge or grainy bread are the best choices, as they help to keep your blood glucose levels stable so you won't feel hungry. And including some protein-rich food like eggs, milk or yoghurt slows the rate at which food is digested so that you tend to feel full for longer.

Eating fruit that is rich in vitamin C, like kiwi fruit, citrus fruit, berries or melon, at breakfast will boost the amount of iron your body absorbs from the cereals, bread and eggs.

fresh vitality pure nourishing luscious healthy balance variety fresh vitality pure nourishing luscious healthy balance variety

golden door porridge

250 g (9 oz/2½ cups) rolled oats
250 ml (9 fl oz/1 cup) skim or soy milk

Put 500 ml (17 fl oz/2 cups) of water in a saucepan and bring to the boil. Add the oats, reduce the heat and simmer for 10 minutes, stirring frequently.

Add the milk and cook for a further 5 minutes, stirring often. Turn off the heat and leave for 3–4 minutes before serving. Delicious with sliced banana and cinnamon or a drizzle of maple syrup.

Serves 6

Nutrition per serve: Energy: 166 kJ (40 Cals); Protein: 0 g; Total fat: 0 g; Carbohydrate: 10 g; Fibre: 2 g; Sodium: 4 mg

stewed fruit compôte

100 g (3½ oz) each of four types of mixed dried fruit (try sultanas, chopped figs, prunes, dates, apricots)

Put the fruit in a saucepan over low heat and cover with water. Bring to the boil slowly. Cover the pan, remove from the heat and leave to cool. Store in the fridge.

Serves 12

CHEF'S TIP: This is something that needs to be cooked slowly. Never stew fruit over high heat or it will scorch and burn.

Nutrition per serve (3 tablespoons): Energy: 87 kJ (21 Cals); Protein: 0 g; Total fat: 0 g; Carbohydrate: 5 g; Fibre: 1 g; Sodium: 2 mg

marmalade

10 navel oranges
125 ml (4 fl oz/½ cup) maple syrup

Zest (or grate the skin off) five of the oranges. Blanch the zest in boiling water for 30 seconds, then refresh under cold water. Blanch and refresh the zest a second time.

Remove the skin and pith from all the oranges. Cut the oranges into small pieces and put in a saucepan with the syrup. Cook gently over low heat for 50 minutes, stirring occasionally, until the oranges are thick and syrupy. Add the zest and cook for a further 5 minutes.

Allow to cool, then transfer to sterilized jars and store in the fridge for up to 2 weeks.

Makes 750 ml (26 fl oz/3 cups)

Nutrition per serve (2 teaspoons): Energy: 52 kJ (12 Cals); Protein: 0 g; Total fat: 0 g; Carbohydrate: 3 g; Fibre: 0 g; Sodium: 1 mg

golden door muesli

300 g (10½ oz/1½ cups) triticale flakes

200 g (7 oz/2 cups) rolled oats

550 g (1 lb 4 oz/3 cups) rolled barley

150 g (5½ oz/1 cup) fine oat bran

85 g (3 oz/½ cup) pepitas (pumpkin seeds)

40 g (¼ cup) sunflower seeds

150 g (5½ oz/1 cup) currants

170 g (6 oz/1 cup) sultanas

3 tablespoons chopped almonds

90 g (3 oz/1 cup) dried apple, chopped

140 g (5 oz/1 cup) dried apricot, chopped

30 g (1 oz/½ cup) psyllium husk

3 tablespoons ground linseed

Mix together all the ingredients in a large bowl. Store the muesli in an airtight container and serve with yoghurt, skim or soy milk and fresh fruit.

Serves 28

Nutrition per serve: Energy: 968 kJ (231 Cals); Protein: 7 g; Total fat: 5 g; Carbohydrate: 41 g; Fibre: 8 g; Sodium: 11 mg

toasted oat muesli

200 g (7 oz/2 cups) rolled oats

2 tablespoons honey

65 g (2½ oz/½ cup) oat bran fibre

50 g (1¾ oz/½ cup) dried apple, chopped

80 g (2¾ oz/½ cup) dried apricots, chopped

100 g (3½ oz/½ cup) sultanas

Preheat the oven to 140°C (275°F/Gas 1). Mix together the oats, honey and 2 tablespoons of water with your fingers to thoroughly combine and spread in a thin layer over a baking tray. Bake in the oven for 30 minutes, until lightly toasted. When cooled, mix with the oat bran and dried fruit and store in an airtight container. Serve with yoghurt, skim or soy milk and fresh fruit.

Serves 8

Nutrition per serve: Energy: 847 kJ (202 Cals); Protein: 5 g; Total fat: 3 g; Carbohydrate: 40 g; Fibre: 5 g; Sodium: 9 mg

golden door muesli (front); toasted oat muesli

gluten-free muesli

225 g (8 oz/3½ cups) rice flakes
75 g (2¾ oz/3 cups) amaranth
115 g (4 oz) rice bran or sticks
3 teaspoons ground linseed
3 tablespoons dried diced pineapple
3 tablespoons dried diced papaya
3 tablespoons pepitas (pumpkin seeds)
3 tablespoons dried banana chips
3 tablespoons sun-dried banana
3 tablespoons sunflower seeds

Mix together all the ingredients and store in an airtight container. Serve with yoghurt, skim or soy milk and fresh fruit.

Serves 10

Nutrition per serve: Energy: 1059 kJ (253 Cals); Protein: 7 g; Total fat: 7 g; Carbohydrate: 38 g; Fibre: 6 g; Sodium: 30 mg

golden door yoghurt

300 g (10½ oz/3 cups) skim milk powder
250 g (9 oz/1 cup) acidophilus bifidis yoghurt

Bring 2½ litres (88 fl oz/10 cups) of water to the boil, then cool to 43°C (110°F). Add the milk powder a little at a time and whisk until dissolved. Add the yoghurt and whisk again. Strain to remove any lumps.

Line the bottom of a large boiler pot with old towels. Cover the bowl of yoghurt and place inside the boiler pot on top of the towels. Tuck more towels between the two pots. Cover with more towels, put the lid on the pot and leave in a warm place for about 6 hours to set.

Serves 12

CHEF'S TIP: Once set, stir in a little fruit coulis (page 187) to make a fruit yoghurt.

Nutrition per serve: Energy: 416 kJ (99 Cals); Protein: 11 g; Total fat: 0 g; Carbohydrate: 14 g; Fibre: 0 g; Sodium: 121 mg

muesli bars

100 g (3½ oz/1 cup) rolled oats
3 tablespoons almonds (optional)
140 g (5 oz/1 cup) dried apricots
90 g (3¼ oz/1 cup) dried apple
180 g (6½ oz/1 cup) pitted dates
60 g (2¼ oz/½ cup) sultanas
2 dried figs
juice of ½ orange

Put all the ingredients except the orange juice in a food processor in batches and mix well.

Add the orange juice a little at a time until the mixture lightly sticks together.

Press the mixture into a small baking tray lined with baking paper. Refrigerate overnight and then cut into 16 small bars to serve.

Serves 16

Nutrition per serve: Energy: 467 kJ (112 Cals); Protein: 2 g; Total fat: 2 g; Carbohydrate: 22 g; Fibre: 3 g; Sodium: 8 mg

berry and yoghurt crunch

300 g (10½ oz/2 cups) golden door muesli (page 33)
500 g (1 lb 2 oz/2 cups) golden door yoghurt (page 34)
100 g (3½ oz/¾ cup) raspberries
100 g (3½ oz/⅔ cup) blueberries
100 g (3½ oz/⅔ cup) strawberries, sliced
2 nectarines, sliced
50 ml (1¾ oz) maple syrup or honey

Spread the muesli evenly over the base of a large flat dish. Spread the yoghurt over the top to cover the muesli. Scatter the berries and nectarines over the yoghurt and then drizzle maple syrup over the fruit.

Serves 8

Nutrition per serve: Energy: 795 kJ (190 Cals); Protein: 7 g; Total fat: 3 g; Carbohydrate: 35 g; Fibre: 6 g; Sodium: 37 mg

apple and berry muffins

1 tablespoon cornflour (cornstarch)

440 g (15½ oz/3½ cups) spelt flour

2 teaspoons bicarbonate of soda (baking soda)

2 apples, peeled and finely chopped

180 g (6½ oz/1 cup) dates, pitted and chopped

235 g (8½ oz/⅔ cup) honey

300 g (10½ oz/2 cups) blueberries or raspberries

Preheat the oven to 180°C (350°F/Gas 4). Mix together the cornflour, spelt flour and bicarbonate of soda in a large bowl. Add the apples, dates and honey and mix together.

Add 410 ml (14 fl oz/1⅔ cups) of water to the dry mixture and fold together. Lightly fold in the berries. The mixture should not be too wet; if it is, add a little more flour.

Lightly spray a 12-hole muffin tin with oil and spoon the mixture into the tin. Bake for about 25 minutes.

Makes 12

Nutrition per muffin: Energy: 1068 kJ (255 Cals); Protein: 6 g; Total fat: 1 g; Carbohydrate: 56 g; Fibre: 7 g; Sodium: 123 mg

banana, pecan and maple muffins

2 apples, peeled and finely chopped

3 ripe bananas, chopped

85 g (3 oz/½ cup) pitted dates, chopped

55 g (2 oz/⅓ cup) sultanas

125 ml (4 fl oz/½ cup) maple syrup

3 tablespoons finely chopped pecan nuts

310 g (11 oz/2½ cups) wholemeal spelt flour

1 teaspoon bicarbonate of soda (baking soda)

1 teaspoon ground cinnamon

Preheat the oven to 180°C (350°F/Gas 4). Mix together all the ingredients by hand until well combined. Add 375 ml (13 fl oz/1½ cups) of water and fold together. The mixture should not be too wet; if it is, add a little more flour.

Lightly spray a 12-hole muffin tin with oil and spoon the mixture into the tin. Bake for about 25 minutes.

Makes 12

Nutrition per muffin: Energy: 889 kJ (212 Cals); Protein: 4 g; Total fat: 3 g; Carbohydrate: 44 g; Fibre: 5 g; Sodium: 52 mg

omelette

1 egg, plus 2 egg whites, lightly beaten

3 tablespoons skim milk

a sprinkling of chopped chives, parsley or other fresh herbs

filling

1 tablespoon grated reduced-fat feta cheese

OR

100 g (3½ oz) tuna in springwater, drained

1 tomato, seeded and chopped

Preheat the grill (broiler) to very hot. Whisk the eggs, milk and herbs in a bowl and season with salt and pepper.

Lightly spray a frying pan with oil and place over medium heat. Add the egg mixture and cook for 30 seconds, until the bottom of the omelette has set, then sprinkle with the feta or tuna and tomato. Put the pan under the hot grill for about 1 minute. Serve hot or cold.

Serves 1

CHEF'S TIP: Instead of using spray oil, cut a circle of baking paper the same size as your frying pan and place in the pan to cover the base completely. Cook as above, turn out the omelette and peel off the paper.

Nutrition per serve (with feta): Energy: 715 kJ (171 Cals); Protein: 21 g; Total fat: 8 g; Carbohydrate: 4 g; Fibre: 0 g; Sodium: 434 mg

Nutrition per serve (with tuna and tomato): Energy: 1020 kJ (244 Cals); Protein: 37 g; Total fat: 7 g; Carbohydrate: 7g; Fibre: 2 g; Sodium: 280 mg

roast tomatoes with basil and balsamic

6 roma (plum) tomatoes
1 tablespoon balsamic vinegar
1 tablespoon chopped fresh basil

Preheat the oven to 200°C (400°F/Gas 6). Trim the stalk ends of the tomatoes and then cut in half lengthways. Put the tomatoes, cut side up, on a baking tray, sprinkle with the balsamic vinegar, basil and salt and pepper to taste. Bake for about 30 minutes.

Serves 6

Nutrition per serve: Energy: 96 kJ (23 Cals); Protein: 2 g; Total fat: 0 g; Carbohydrate: 3 g; Fibre: 2 g; Sodium: 10 mg

fruit loaf

6 dried apricots

250 ml (9 fl oz/1 cup) orange juice

400 g (14 oz) mixed dried fruit (try sultanas, currants or raisins)

1 teaspoon mixed spice

1 teaspoon ground cinnamon

260 g (9¼ oz/1 cup) cold mashed pumpkin

200 g (7 oz/1⅔ cups) spelt flour

3 teaspoons baking powder

Put the apricots and orange juice in a saucepan and bring to the boil. Turn off the heat and leave the apricots to soften. Once soft, put in a blender and blend until smooth.

Return the apricots to the saucepan and add the mixed fruit and spices. Bring back to the boil and then turn off the heat. Transfer to a mixing bowl and leave to cool completely. Preheat the oven to 160°C (315°F/Gas 2–3).

Lightly spray a 10 x 20 cm (4 x 8 inch) loaf tin with oil and then line with baking paper.

Add the pumpkin to the fruit mix and stir through thoroughly. Add the spelt flour and baking powder and mix well.

Bake for 1 hour 20 minutes, covering the loaf with foil for the last 45 minutes. Turn out onto a wire rack to cool before serving.

Serves 15

Nutrition per serve: Energy: 561 kJ (134 Cals); Protein: 3 g; Total fat: 0.5 g; Carbohydrate: 30 g; Fibre: 2 g; Sodium: 70 mg

noon

noon

Eating regular meals and making the right food choices will help you feel focused and energized throughout the day. Many people complain of an afternoon 'slump' when they feel sleepy, lack concentration and give in to sugar cravings. They're not imagining this: it is caused by a fall in blood glucose levels and is usually the result of skipping breakfast or lunch, over-eating at lunch time or eating the wrong types of carbohydrates (highly processed or high GI carbohydrates).

Some people argue that breakfast and lunch should be the biggest meals of the day, keeping the evening meal light. In reality, the time at which you eat your main meal does not matter. What counts is your total energy intake over the course of the day. It is also important that you eat regularly, not skipping meals and not over-eating to compensate. And for many people it is simply more convenient to eat a quick light lunch and have their largest meal in the evening when they have more time to relax.

Our noon recipes are packed with nutrients and a healthy balance of carbohydrate and protein to keep your blood glucose levels stable and leave you feeling great all through the afternoon.

fresh vitality pure nourishing luscious
healthy balance variety fresh vitality pure
nourishing luscious healthy balance variety

pearl barley and kidney bean soup

3 tablespoons raw pearl barley, soaked overnight

85 g (3 oz/½ cup) kidney beans, soaked overnight

½ teaspoon mustard seed oil or olive oil

1 white onion, chopped

85 g (3 oz/½ cup) diced peeled sweet potato

3 tablespoons diced celery root (or celery)

3 tablespoons diced leek, white part only

2 garlic cloves

2 sprigs fresh rosemary

2 teaspoons fine polenta

750 ml (26 fl oz/3 cups) vegetable stock (page 170)

1 tomato, diced

2 tablespoons snipped chives

Rinse the pearl barley and kidney beans and then boil in separate pans of water until tender (the barley will need about 15 minutes and the beans about 25 minutes). Drain.

Heat the oil in a large stockpot and add the onion, sweet potato, celery root and leek and fry over low heat for 3 minutes.

Add the garlic, rosemary, polenta, stock, barley and kidney beans and boil gently for 20 minutes.

Add the tomato and chives just before serving.

Serves 4

Nutrition per serve: Energy: 517 kJ (124 Cals); Protein: 8 g; Total fat: 1 g; Carbohydrate: 20 g; Fibre: 1 g; Sodium: 132 mg

caesar salad

dressing

250 ml (9 fl oz/1 cup) golden door
yoghurt (page 34)

3 garlic cloves, roasted (page 113)

2 tablespoons lemon juice

125 g (4½ oz/½ cup) wholegrain
mustard

2 tablespoons apple juice concentrate

¼ teaspoon sea salt

cracked black pepper, to taste

croutons

2 garlic cloves, roasted (page 113)

2 tablespoons chopped fresh rosemary

1 tablespoon lemon juice

150 g (5½ oz) Turkish bread, cut into
small cubes

300 g (10½ oz) firm tofu,
cut into small strips

3 tablespoons tamari soy sauce

6 free-range eggs

2 tablespoons brown vinegar

2 cos lettuce, roughly chopped

1 small red onion, thinly sliced

To make the dressing, put all the ingredients in a blender and process until smooth. This will make 450 ml (16 fl oz) of dressing that will keep in the fridge for up to a week.

To make the croutons, preheat the oven to 200°C (400°F/Gas 6). Put the garlic, rosemary, lemon juice and 2 tablespoons of water in a blender and mix until smooth. Season with salt and pepper. Brush over the bread cubes.

Put the bread croutons on a paper-lined baking tray and bake for 15 minutes or until golden. Stir the croutons frequently while they are baking.

Put the tofu on a paper-lined baking tray and sprinkle with the tamari, making sure the tofu is covered. Bake for 30 minutes or until firm, stirring occasionally so that the tofu cooks evenly.

To poach the eggs, bring to the boil 5 cm (2 inches) of water in a frying pan and add the vinegar (this will prevent the eggs spreading too much in the water). Reduce to a simmer. Stir the water gently, then break the eggs into the water. Cook the eggs for approximately 3 minutes, or until they are soft-poached, then remove with a slotted spoon.

Divide the lettuce, onion, tofu and croutons among six bowls, top each salad with a poached egg and drizzle with a tablespoon of dressing.

Serves 6

Nutrition per serve: Energy: 977 kJ (233 Cals); Protein: 18 g;
Total fat: 10 g; Carbohydrate: 16 g; Fibre: 4 g; Sodium: 715 mg

nori rolls with ponzu sauce

330 g (11¾ oz/1½ cups) white short-grain rice

3 tablespoons mirin

2 teaspoons brown rice vinegar

1 packet nori sheets

fillings

1 avocado, cut into thin wedges

1 mango, sliced

350 g (12 oz/2 bunches) asparagus, blanched and sliced diagonally

1 red capsicum (pepper), cut into thin strips

2 teaspoons sesame seeds

ponzu sauce

2 tablespoons sesame seeds

100 ml (3½ fl oz) ponzu sauce

1 teaspoon fresh lime juice

Put the rice in a saucepan and cover with 750 ml (26 fl oz/ 3 cups) of water. Bring to the boil, reduce the heat and simmer for 15 minutes. Turn out into a shallow dish and pour the mirin and vinegar over the top. Leave to cool.

Lay a nori sheet, shiny side down, on a bamboo mat. Cover the nori with a layer of rice, leaving a 1 cm (½ inch) clear border at the top of the nori. Arrange your choice of fillings about 2.5 cm (1 inch) from the bottom edge of the nori and then roll up inside the bamboo mat. Start with the edge closest to you, making sure to apply even pressure all the way along the bamboo mat while rolling.

Leave the sushi, seam side down, to settle for 15 minutes and then cut into even pieces with a very sharp knife. Serve with ponzu or soy sauce for dipping.

To make the ponzu sauce, lightly toast the sesame seeds for a few seconds in a dry pan over high heat. Remove from the pan immediately to prevent burning. Mix with the ponzu sauce and lime juice.

Serves 10

CHEF'S TIP: Any leftover nori sheets will keep in the fridge for 2 days, wrapped in plastic in an airtight container. For variation, or to increase the protein in this dish, add thin strips of fresh salmon or tuna to the filling.

Nutrition per serve: Energy: 864 kJ (206 Cals); Protein: 5 g; Total fat: 7 g; Carbohydrate: 28 g; Fibre: 4 g; Sodium: 209 mg

vegetable soup with garlic and lemon croutons

1½ litres (52 fl oz/6 cups) vegetable stock (page 170)

1 litre (35 fl oz/4 cups) low-fat soy milk

750 g (1 lb 10 oz/4 cups) red lentils

350 g (12 oz) mushrooms, finely sliced

1 large onion, coarsely grated or julienned

1 large carrot, coarsely grated or julienned

1 swede, coarsely grated or julienned

3 tablespoons snipped garlic chives

croutons

2 garlic cloves

1 tablespoon lemon juice

150 g (5½ oz) Turkish bread, cut into small cubes

1 tablespoon chopped fresh coriander (cilantro)

Put the stock and milk in a pan and bring to the boil. Add the lentils and stir until boiling. Add the remaining vegetables and bring back to the boil. Reduce the heat and simmer for 30 minutes, stirring occasionally, until the lentils and vegetables are breaking up. Season to taste and then blend the soup until smooth. Add the chives just before serving.

Meanwhile, to make the croutons, preheat the oven to 200°C (400°F/Gas 6). Put the garlic and lemon juice in a blender with 2 tablespoons of water and salt and pepper to taste. Blend until smooth. Toss the bread in the mixture and then arrange on a baking tray and bake for 15 minutes. Toss with the coriander and then serve sprinkled over the soup.

Serves 16

CHEF'S TIP: Soup is great to make in large quantities. This one freezes well; for best results, blend it again after thawing. The croutons cannot be frozen: make them fresh while you are reheating the soup.

Nutrition per serve: Energy: 768 kJ (183 Cals); Protein: 16 g; Total fat: 2 g; Carbohydrate: 27 g; Fibre: 9 g; Sodium: 138 mg

ocean trout spring rolls with ginger and coriander

20 spring roll wrappers

1 Chinese cabbage, finely shredded

750 g (1 lb 10 oz) ocean trout fillet, cut into strips

50 g (1¾ oz) pickled ginger

350 g (12 oz/2 bunches) asparagus, cut in half

½ bunch fresh coriander (cilantro), chopped

1 egg white, lightly beaten

Preheat the oven to 200ºC (400ºF/Gas 6). Place the spring roll wrappers on a dry work surface. Put some shredded cabbage on the bottom corner of each wrapper and arrange the fish, ginger, asparagus and coriander over the cabbage.

Start rolling the wrapper from the bottom corner over the filling and continue rolling until you are halfway up. Fold in the left and right sides to enclose the filling and then roll up to the top.

Put the rolls on a baking tray and lightly brush with egg white. Bake for about 15 minutes.

Makes 20

CHEF'S TIP: You could use 750 g (1 lb 10 oz) prawns (shrimp) or chicken, cut into strips, instead of the trout.

Nutrition per roll: Energy: 371 kJ (89 Cals); Protein: 10 g; Total fat: 2 g; Carbohydrate: 8 g; Fibre: 1 g; Sodium: 72 mg

roasted beetroot with orange dressing

6 baby beetroot, peeled and quartered
1 red onion, finely sliced
juice of 3 oranges
3 tablespoons balsamic vinegar
2 tablespoons apple juice concentrate
1 teaspoon cornflour (cornstarch)
1 orange, segmented

Preheat the oven to 200°C (400°F/Gas 6). Put the beetroot, onion, orange juice, vinegar, apple juice and a pinch of salt in a baking dish. Bake for 45 minutes, or until the beetroot is tender (if the beetroot seems to be drying out, add a little water).

Lift out the beetroot, drain the juice into a saucepan and bring to the boil. Mix the cornflour with 2 teaspoons of water until smooth and add to the pan. Bring back to the boil, stirring until smooth, then cool. Arrange the beetroot on a serving dish and cover with the glaze. Toss with the orange segments to serve.

Serves 6 as a side dish

Nutrition per serve: Energy: 225 kJ (54 Cals); Protein: 1 g;
Total fat: 0 g; Carbohydrate: 12 g; Fibre: 2 g; Sodium: 26 mg

apple salad with coconut and lime dressing

dressing

2 tablespoons lemon juice

2 tablespoons apple juice concentrate

3 tablespoons shredded makrut (kaffir lime) leaves

3 tablespoons shredded coconut

90 g (3¼ oz/1 cup) bean sprouts

¼ cucumber, chopped

1 small red capsicum (pepper), sliced

45 g (1¾ oz/½ cup) mung bean sprouts

12 cherry tomatoes, halved

3 red apples, peeled and sliced

To make the dressing, put the lemon juice, apple concentrate and lime leaves in a blender with a pinch of salt and blend well. Add the coconut. Mix together all the salad ingredients and toss with the dressing. Serve immediately.

Serves 6 as a side dish

Nutrition per serve: Energy: 348 kJ (83 Cals); Protein: 2 g; Total fat: 2 g; Carbohydrate: 14 g; Fibre: 3 g; Sodium: 11 mg

couscous pancakes with lentil and capsicum caponata

3 tablespoons puy or green lentils

2 roma (plum) tomatoes, halved

4 tablespoons couscous

3 eggs, separated

3 tablespoons skim milk

2 tablespoons wholemeal flour

60 g (2¼ oz/½ cup) plain (all-purpose) flour

1 teaspoon olive oil

¼ onion, chopped

1 garlic clove, chopped

¼ red capsicum (pepper), diced

¼ yellow capsicum (pepper), diced

¼ small eggplant (aubergine), diced

375 ml (13 fl oz/1½ cups) tomato pasta sauce (page 179)

85 g (3 oz) reduced-fat feta cheese, crumbled

Put the lentils in a pan of boiling water and simmer for 15–20 minutes until tender. Drain and set aside. Grill (broil) the tomato halves under a hot grill for 5 minutes. Put the couscous in a bowl with 4 tablespoons of boiling water, cover very tightly and leave for 3 minutes. Stir to fluff up the couscous.

Beat together the egg yolks and milk and then fold in the flours. Beat the egg whites until soft peaks form and fold through the mixture. Set the batter aside.

Heat the oil in a saucepan and add the onion, garlic, capsicum, eggplant and tomato sauce. Cook for 5 minutes and then stir in the lentils. Keep warm.

Heat a non-stick frying pan and spray with oil. Spoon half the pancake batter into the pan to form four pancakes. Cook for 2 minutes until just set, then sprinkle with half the couscous. Flip over and cook the other side for 2 minutes. Remove from the pan and repeat with the remaining batter to make another four pancakes.

Place a pancake on each plate and spoon the lentil caponata over the top. Sprinkle with a spoonful of feta and top with another pancake. Top with a grilled tomato half and serve immediately.

Serves 4

Nutrition per serve: Energy: 1169 kJ (279 Cals); Protein: 19 g; Total fat: 10 g; Carbohydrate: 29 g; Fibre: 5 g; Sodium: 345 mg

tofu stir-fry with buckwheat noodles

125 g (4 oz) buckwheat noodles
1 teaspoon sesame oil
400 g (14 oz) tofu, diced
1 small carrot, julienned
300 g (10½ oz/4 cups) chopped Asian vegetables (bok choy, snow peas etc)
2 garlic cloves, sliced
1 chilli, finely chopped
2 tablespoons tamari soy sauce
1 teaspoon cornflour (cornstarch)
2 teaspoons sweet chilli sauce

Cook the noodles in boiling water according to the packet instructions. Set aside. Heat up a wok or non-stick frying pan and add the sesame oil. When hot, add the tofu and fry for 5–10 minutes until slightly crisp. Remove from the wok.

Add the carrot, Asian vegetables, garlic and chilli to the wok with 1 teaspoon of water and toss for 2 minutes until wilted. Add the tamari. Mix the cornflour with 2 teaspoons of water and add to the wok. Add the chilli sauce, noodles and tofu and toss together before serving.

Serves 4

Nutrition per serve: Energy: 1129 kJ (270 cal); Protein: 18 g; Total fat: 9 g; Carbohydrate: 28 g; Fibre: 8 g; Sodium: 420 mg

thai beef salad

1 tablespoon fish sauce

juice of 2 limes

pinch of caster (superfine) sugar

2 teaspoons tamari soy sauce

**small handful fresh coriander (cilantro)
leaves, chopped**

150 g (5½ oz) cherry tomatoes

100 g (3½ oz) rice noodles

**125 g (4½ oz/1½ cups) chopped green
beans, snake beans or French beans**

160 g (6 oz) beef fillet

Mix together the fish sauce, lime juice, sugar, soy sauce and chopped coriander. Crush the cherry tomatoes into the dressing and leave to marinate.

Meanwhile, cook the rice noodles in 500 ml (17 fl oz/ 2 cups) of boiling water for 4–5 minutes. Drain and refresh in cold water, then add to the marinade with the beans.

Cut the beef fillet into four even pieces and grill (broil) or pan-fry for 2 minutes on each side.

Divide the noodles among four plates. Cut the beef into thin even slices and arrange on top of the noodles. Drizzle any remaining dressing over the top before serving.

Serves 4

Nutrition per serve: Energy: 692 kJ (165 cal); Protein: 12 g; Total fat: 2 g; Carbohydrate: 23 g; Fibre: 3 g; Sodium: 610 mg

wok-seared soba noodles with chicken and black beans

125 g (4½ oz) soba noodles

1 teaspoon sesame seed oil

250 g (9 oz) chicken breast, cut into thin strips

80 g (2¾ oz/½ cup) chopped carrot

80 g (2¾ oz/½ cup) chopped capsicum (pepper)

½ small onion, chopped

1 teaspoon chopped garlic

1 teaspoon chopped fresh ginger

40 g (1½ oz/½ cup) chopped mushrooms

1 tablespoon tamari soy sauce

125 ml (4 fl oz/½ cup) chicken stock

1 tablespoon sweet chilli sauce

1 tablespoon Asian black beans, rinsed and crushed

40 g (1½ oz/½ cup) baby spinach

Cook the soba noodles according to the directions on the packet, then drain.

Heat a wok or non-stick frying pan and add the sesame oil. When hot, add the chicken and fry until golden. Add the carrot, capsicum, onion, garlic, ginger and mushrooms and stir-fry for 2 minutes. Add the soy sauce, stock, chilli sauce and black beans and cook for 1 minute.

Add the noodles and spinach to the wok and toss to heat through before serving.

Serves 4

Nutrition per serve: Energy: 961 kJ (230 Cals); Protein: 18 g; Total fat: 5 g; Carbohydrate: 27 g; Fibre: 2 g; Sodium: 325 mg

pumpkin and rocket cannelloni

1 kg (2 lb 4 oz) pumpkin (squash)
1 teaspoon olive oil
½ small onion, diced
½ garlic clove, minced
8 basil leaves, torn
160 g (6 oz) firm tofu, minced
80 g (3 oz) reduced-fat ricotta cheese
40 g (1½ oz/1 cup) rocket (arugula)
4 large fresh lasagne sheets, cut in half
250 ml (9 fl oz/1 cup) tomato pasta sauce (page 179)
4 roma (plum) tomatoes, roasted (page 113)

Preheat the oven to 200°C (400°F/Gas 6). Slice the pumpkin and arrange on a paper-lined baking tray. Bake for 45 minutes until softened and then mash (you should have about 2 cups of mash). Reduce the oven to 180°C (350°F/Gas 4).

Heat up a frying pan, add the olive oil and fry the onion until golden brown. Add the garlic. Add the mashed pumpkin and cook for 5–10 minutes over low heat. Add the basil leaves, tofu and ricotta and mix well. Add the rocket and leave to cool.

Lay the eight sheets of pasta on the work surface and divide the filling among them. Roll up into tubes and place in a lightly oiled ovenproof dish. Pour the tomato sauce over the top and bake for 20 minutes. Serve with the roasted tomatoes and a side salad.

Serves 4

CHEF'S TIP: Use wholemeal lasagne sheets if you can find them. Those with gluten intolerance can still enjoy this recipe by using gluten-free pasta.

Nutrition per serve: Energy: 1173 kJ (280 Cals); Protein: 17 g; Total fat: 8 g; Carbohydrate: 34 g; Fibre: 9 g; Sodium: 141 mg

vietnamese spring rolls

dipping sauce

1 tablespoon tamari soy sauce

1 tablespoon fish sauce

2 teaspoons caster (superfine) or palm sugar (jaggery)

2 tablespoons pickled ginger

1 garlic clove, crushed

1 teaspoon lemon juice

1 teaspoon lime juice

½ teaspoon chopped chilli

100 g (3½ oz) bean thread noodles

40 g (1½ oz/½ cup) shredded Chinese cabbage

1 small carrot, julienned

90 g (3¼ oz/1 cup) bean sprouts

½ small red capsicum (pepper), julienned

½ small cucumber, julienned

2 tablespoons chopped roasted peanuts

2 teaspoons shredded fresh mint

8 spring roll wrappers

160 g (6 oz) firm tofu, cut into 8 strips

To make the dipping sauce, mix together the soy sauce, fish sauce, sugar, ginger, garlic, lemon and lime juices and chilli.

Soak the noodles in water for 5 minutes to soften, then drain. Mix together all the vegetables, noodles, peanuts and mint. Add a quarter of the dipping sauce and mix gently. Leave to marinate. Keep the rest of the dipping sauce to serve in individual bowls.

Quickly soak the spring roll wrappers in warm water to soften them and place one at a time on a dry tea towel. Divide the filling into eight portions and place one at the bottom edge of each wrapper. Add a strip of tofu.

Start rolling the wrapper from the bottom edge over the filling and continue rolling until you are halfway up. Fold in the left and right sides to enclose the filling and then roll up to the top. Serve two rolls per person with a bowl of dipping sauce.

Serves 4

Nutrition per serve: Energy: 1175 kJ (281 cal); Protein: 12 g; Total fat: 6 g; Carbohydrate: 45 g; Fibre: 4 g; Sodium: 693 mg

feta, sweet potato and eggplant frittata

100 g (3½ oz) eggplant (aubergine)
200 g (7 oz) sweet potato, peeled
½ teaspoon olive oil
¼ onion, chopped
1 garlic clove, chopped
¼ capsicum (pepper), diced
5 free-range eggs
185 ml (6 fl oz/¾ cup) skim milk
110 g (3¾ oz/½ cup) hummus (page 182)
125 ml (4 fl oz/½ cup) low-fat yoghurt
80 g (2¾ oz) low-fat feta, crumbled
freshly ground black pepper
½ teaspoon celery salt
40 g (1½ oz/½ cup) baby spinach
80 g (2¾ oz/½ cup) zucchini (courgette) slices

Preheat the oven to 170°C (325°F/Gas 3). Slice the eggplant and sweet potato and arrange on a paper-lined baking tray. Bake for 30 minutes until softened and then cut into small cubes.

Heat the oil in a frying pan and fry the onion, garlic and capsicum until softened.

Beat together the eggs, milk, hummus, yoghurt, feta, pepper and celery salt. Lightly oil four 250 ml (9 fl oz/ 1 cup) quiche dishes and divide all the cooked vegetables, the spinach and zucchini among them. Pour the egg mixture over the top and bake for 35–40 minutes.

Serves 4

Nutrition per serve: Energy: 1046 kJ (250 Cals); Protein: 21 g; Total fat: 11 g; Carbohydrate: 16 g; Fibre: 3 g; Sodium: 480 mg

wholemeal spaghetti with goat's cheese, lemon and hummus sauce

250 g (9 oz) wholemeal spaghetti

125 ml (4 fl oz/½ cup) skim milk

1 teaspoon cornflour (cornstarch)

1 tablespoon hummus (page 182)

20 cherry tomatoes, halved

85 g (3 oz/1 cup) baby spinach

½ small zucchini (courgette), shredded

¼ teaspoon lemon zest

4 tablespoons crumbled goat's cheese

1 teaspoon shredded fresh basil

Cook the pasta in a large pan of boiling water until *al dente*. Drain well.

Meanwhile, warm the milk gently in a pan. Mix the cornflour with 2 teaspoons of water until smooth and then add to the milk with the hummus. Bring to the boil and then reduce the heat to a simmer.

Add the cherry tomatoes, spinach, zucchini and lemon zest. Toss the sauce through the cooked spaghetti, add the goat's cheese and basil and serve immediately.

Serves 4

CHEF'S TIP: Those with a gluten intolerance can still enjoy this recipe by using gluten-free pasta.

Nutrition per serve: Energy: 1042 kJ (249 Cals); Protein: 11 g; Total fat: 3 g; Carbohydrate: 43 g; Fibre: 8 g; Sodium: 87 mg

calzone pizzas

10 g (¼ oz) fresh yeast

2 drops apple juice concentrate

100 g (3½ oz) plain (all-purpose) flour

100 g (3½ oz) wholemeal flour

2 teaspoons extra virgin olive oil

½ teaspoon salt

4 tablespoons tomato pasta sauce (page 179)

1 tablespoon chopped fresh parsley

2 artichoke hearts, quartered

2 mushrooms, sliced

40 g (1½ oz/½ cup) baby spinach

2 tablespoons reduced-fat ricotta

1 egg, lightly beaten

Mix the yeast and apple concentrate with 1 tablespoon of warm water. Mix together the flours and make a well in the centre. Pour the oil, salt, yeast mixture and 125 ml (4 fl oz/½ cup) of water into the well and knead together to form a soft dough. Cover the dough and leave to rest for 15 minutes. Preheat the oven to 200°C (400°F/Gas 6).

Divide the dough into four portions and roll each one out to make a 20 cm (8 inch) circle.

Mix together the tomato sauce and chopped parsley and spread a tablespoon over each pizza. Arrange the artichoke, mushrooms and spinach over the pizzas, keeping the filling on one half of the pizza. Mix the ricotta with the egg and spoon a quarter onto each pizza, over the other fillings. Fold the empty half of the pizza over the top and crimp the edge to seal. Bake for 15–20 minutes.

Serves 4

Nutrition per serve: Energy: 1005 kJ (240 Cals); Protein: 10 g; Total fat: 6 g; Carbohydrate: 36 g; Fibre: 6 g; Sodium: 448 mg

linguine with roasted pumpkin and avocado pesto

150 g (5½ oz) pumpkin (squash), diced

½ teaspoon trocomare (herb salt)

300 g (10½ oz) linguine

200 g (7 oz) baby spinach

1 red capsicum (pepper), roasted, peeled and cut into strips

175 g (6 oz/1 bunch) asparagus, blanched and sliced diagonally

100 g (3½ oz) baby button mushrooms

2 tablespoons lemon juice

1 tablespoon white balsamic vinegar

4 tablespoons avocado pesto (page 186)

Preheat the oven to 200°C (400°F/Gas 6). Put the pumpkin on a paper-lined baking tray, sprinkle with trocomare and roast for 25 minutes.

Cook the pasta in a large pan of boiling water until *al dente*. Drain and place in a large bowl with the spinach, capsicum and asparagus.

Pan-fry the button mushrooms with the lemon juice, balsamic vinegar and a pinch of salt and pepper for about 1 minute, constantly stirring until the mushrooms are just tender. Add to the pasta with the pumpkin and mix together.

Add the pesto and stir through until the pasta is coated. Serve with more pesto on top if you like.

Serves 4

CHEF'S TIP: Those with a gluten intolerance can still enjoy this recipe by using gluten-free pasta.

Nutrition per serve: Energy: 1449 kJ (346 Cals); Protein: 15 g; Total fat: 9 g; Carbohydrate: 51 g; Fibre: 12 g; Sodium: 269 mg

thai fish cakes on quinoa

160 g (6 oz) snapper fillet, bones and skin removed

160 g (6 oz) salmon fillet, bones and skin removed

160 g (6 oz) peeled raw prawns (shrimp)

2 teaspoons chopped fresh coriander (cilantro)

3 teaspoons fish sauce

2 teaspoons sweet chilli sauce

3 egg whites

1 garlic clove, finely chopped

2 makrut (kaffir lime) leaves, shredded

zest and juice of 1 lemon

1 tablespoon avocado oil

100 g (½ cup) quinoa

zest and juice of ½ lemon

small handful fresh coriander (cilantro) leaves, chopped

Finely chop the snapper, salmon and prawns in a food processor. Add the coriander, fish sauce, chilli sauce, egg whites, garlic, lime leaves, lemon zest and juice and avocado oil. Mix together briefly. Shape into 8 patties.

Lightly oil a non-stick frying pan and cook the patties in batches for 3 minutes on each side.

Meanwhile, wash the quinoa in plenty of cold water and drain. Put in a saucepan with 250 ml (9 fl oz/1 cup) of water. Bring to the boil and then reduce the heat, cover the pan and simmer for 10–12 minutes until all the water has been absorbed. Leave to stand for 5 minutes, then mix with the lemon zest, juice and coriander. Serve the fish cakes on a bed of quinoa.

Serves 4

CHEF'S TIP: Quinoa is an old South American grain with the best amino acid profile of all the grains. It is available from health food stores.

Nutrition per serve: Energy: 1168 kJ (279 cal); Protein: 31 g; Total fat: 10 g; Carbohydrate: 15 g; Fibre: 3 g; Sodium: 591 mg

blue-eye cod curry

1 teaspoon mustard seed oil

1 teaspoon brown mustard seeds

8 curry leaves

spice mix (¼ teaspoon each of fennel seeds, coriander seeds, chilli powder and turmeric)

375 ml (13 fl oz/1½ cups) fish stock (page 171)

1 teaspoon tamarind paste

2 tablespoons low-fat yoghurt

2 tablespoons reduced-fat coconut milk

1 teaspoon besan (chickpea flour)

2 baby bok choy

2 tomatoes, diced

400 g (14 oz) cod, boned and diced

Heat the mustard seed oil in a pan and add the mustard seeds, curry leaves and spice mix. Stir over the heat for a minute until aromatic. Add the fish stock and tamarind and bring to the boil.

Mix together the yoghurt, coconut milk and besan and add to the pan. Whisk together and simmer for 5 minutes. Add the bok choy, tomato and fish and simmer for 5 minutes. Season to taste and serve over steamed brown rice.

Serves 4

CHEF'S TIP: You can use peeled raw prawns (shrimp) instead of the fish.

Nutrition per serve: Energy: 488 kJ (117 Cals); Protein: 20 g; Total fat: 3 g; Carbohydrate: 3 g; Fibre: 2 g; Sodium: 108 mg

roasted cherry tomato and feta tarts

250 g (9 oz) cherry tomatoes, halved

3 small button mushrooms, sliced

1 red onion, finely chopped

3 garlic cloves, finely chopped

2 egg yolks and 8 egg whites

small handful of fresh basil,
finely chopped

3 asparagus spears, chopped

4 sheets spring roll pastry

30 g (1 oz) low-fat feta cheese

3 spring onions (scallions),
finely chopped

Preheat the oven to 170°C (325°F/Gas 3).

Put the tomatoes, mushrooms and onion on a paper-lined baking tray. Sprinkle the garlic and a large pinch of salt and pepper over the top and bake for 20 minutes.

Lightly beat the egg whites and yolks together with the basil and asparagus. Season with salt and pepper. Place a sheet of the pastry on a board and cut into four squares. Layer the pastry squares in a 10 cm (4 inch) pie dish. Repeat with the other pastry sheets and another three pie dishes.

Spoon the roasted vegetables into the dishes and pour the egg mixture over the top. Sprinkle with the feta and spring onions and bake for 30–35 minutes, or until set.

Serves 4

Nutrition per serve: Energy: 617 kJ (147 Cals); Protein: 14 g;
Total fat: 4 g; Carbohydrate: 14 g; Fibre: 3 g; Sodium: 419 mg

italian salad with baked salmon and prawns

1 lemon

4 salmon fillets (each about 130 g/ 4½ oz), skin removed

180 g (6 oz) fresh fettucine

180 g (6 oz) broccolini, stems sliced diagonally, florets intact

4 asparagus spears, sliced diagonally

2 spring onions (scallions), sliced diagonally

2 roma (plum) tomatoes, chopped

8 semi-dried tomatoes (not in oil), chopped

1 tablespoon chopped fresh parsley

1 tablespoon chopped fresh basil

8 cooked prawns (shrimp), peeled

Preheat the oven to 200°C (400°F/Gas 6). Cut the lemon in half and juice one half. Slice the other half. Put the fish on a paper-lined baking tray and sprinkle with the lemon juice and a little salt and pepper. Bake for 8 minutes, then remove from the oven and leave to rest for 2 minutes.

Cook the fettucine in a large pan of boiling water for 7 minutes. Add the broccolini and asparagus and cook for another minute. Drain and set aside.

Heat a saucepan and add the spring onions and a little water. Sprinkle with salt and pepper and cook for about 30 seconds, then add the tomatoes and semi-dried tomatoes and cook for a further 2 minutes. Finally add the fresh herbs and toss with the pasta and vegetables.

Arrange the fettucine salad on each serving plate, top with a piece of salmon and garnish with prawns and slices of lemon.

Serves 4

CHEF'S TIP: An alternative and easy method for cooking fish is to put it on a preheated sandwich grill, sprinkle with a little lemon juice, salt and pepper, close the grill and cook for about 3 minutes.
Those with a gluten intolerance can still enjoy this recipe by using gluten-free pasta.

Nutrition per serve: Energy: 1418 kJ (339 cal); Protein: 40 g; Total fat: 11 g; Carbohydrate: 19 g; Fibre: 6 g; Sodium: 248 mg

coriander crab cakes
with sweet chilli dipping sauce

500 g (1 lb 2 oz) fresh crab meat
200 g (7 oz) ocean trout
½ tablespoon Thai red curry paste
1 egg white
1 spring onion (scallion), chopped
1 tablespoon chopped fresh coriander (cilantro)
1 teaspoon finely chopped lemon grass
½ red Thai chilli, seeded and quartered

sweet chilli sauce (page 186), to serve

Preheat the oven to 180°C (350°F/Gas 4). Put all the ingredients in a food processor and mix until just combined. Take care not to overmix.

Shape level tablespoons of the mixture into patties. Place on a paper-lined baking tray and bake for 10–15 minutes. Serve with sweet chilli sauce and a salad.

Serves 4

CHEF'S TIP: Once you have shaped the mixture into patties you can roll it in sesame seeds before baking.

Nutrition per serve: Energy: 695 kJ (166 Cals); Protein: 26 g; Total fat: 3 g; Carbohydrate: 9 g; Fibre: 0 g; Sodium: 556 mg

orange and fennel salad

3 oranges, peeled and segmented

200 g (7 oz) snow pea sprouts, trimmed

1 red capsicum (pepper), julienned

100 g (3½ oz) rocket (arugula) or baby spinach

1 fennel bulb, thinly sliced

dressing

2 tablespoons lemon juice

2 tablespoons apple juice concentrate

3 tablespoons shredded makrut (kaffir lime) leaves

3 tablespoons shredded coconut

Put the salad ingredients in a bowl and toss together. Put the lemon juice, apple concentrate and lime leaves in a blender with a pinch of salt and blend well. Add the coconut and toss with the salad.

Serves 6 as a side dish

Nutrition per serve: Energy: 363 kJ (87 Cals); Protein: 4 g; Total fat: 2 g; Carbohydrate: 13 g; Fibre: 5 g; Sodium: 25 mg

red cabbage and toasted seed salad

1 tablespoon pepitas (pumpkin seeds)

1 tablespoon sunflower seeds

2 tablespoons currants

2 teaspoons tamari soy sauce

¼ small red cabbage, very finely sliced

100 g (3½ oz) snow pea sprouts, trimmed

1 small red onion, finely sliced

Toast the seeds in a dry frying pan over high heat. While still hot, add the currants and tamari. Mix with the cabbage, sprouts and onion and serve.

Serves 4 as a side dish

Nutrition per serve: Energy: 288 kJ (69 Cals); Protein: 4 g; Total fat: 3 g; Carbohydrate: 7 g; Fibre: 4 g; Sodium: 102 mg

lime, mango and mint couscous

250 ml (9 fl oz/1 cup) vegetable stock
(page 170)

185 g (6½ oz/1 cup) couscous

zest of 1 lime

½ teaspoon chopped fresh mint

½ mango, diced

Put the stock in a pan and bring to the boil. Remove from the heat and add the couscous, lime zest and mint. Stir, cover and leave for about 3 minutes. Fluff up the couscous, stir in the diced mango and serve immediately.

Serves 4 as a side dish

Nutrition per serve: Energy: 775 kJ (185 Cals); Protein: 6 g; Total fat: 0 g; Carbohydrate: 39 g; Fibre: 1 g; Sodium: 5 mg

mediterranean pasta salad with red capsicum sauce

300 g (10½ oz) penne

4 asparagus spears, blanched and sliced diagonally

4 roma (plum) tomatoes, roughly chopped

1 red capsicum (pepper), roasted, peeled and sliced

85 g (3 oz/1 cup) baby spinach

3 tablespoons chopped fresh basil

12 kalamata olives

2 tablespoons snipped chives

¼ teaspoon chopped chilli

1 quantity red capsicum sauce
(page 181)

25 g (1 oz) reduced-fat feta cheese, grated

1 tablespoon pine nuts

Cook the penne in a large pan of boiling water until *al dente*. Drain and cool a little.

Mix the pasta gently with the asparagus, tomatoes, capsicum, spinach, basil, olives, chives and chilli. Add the sauce and stir through. Garnish with the feta and pine nuts to serve.

Serves 4

CHEF'S TIP: Those with a gluten intolerance can still enjoy this recipe by using gluten-free pasta.

Nutrition per serve: Energy: 925 kJ (221 Cals); Protein: 10 g; Total fat: 5 g; Carbohydrate: 34 g; Fibre: 8 g; Sodium: 392mg

picnic prawn and pesto wraps

4 pitta breads

4 tablespoons avocado pesto (page 186)

1 butter lettuce, shredded

1 red capsicum (pepper), roasted, peeled and sliced

8 asparagus spears, blanched

16 cooked prawns (shrimp), peeled

2 tablespoons chopped fresh coriander (cilantro)

Spread the pitta bread with pesto, then add the lettuce, capsicum, asparagus, prawns and coriander. Season with salt and pepper, then roll up and serve.

Serves 4

Nutrition per serve: Energy: 1343 kJ (321 Cals); Protein: 25 g; Total fat: 7 g; Carbohydrate: 39 g; Fibre: 8 g; Sodium: 734 mg

butternut, corn and feta tarts

4 sheets spring roll pastry

100 g (3½ oz/½ cup) grated butternut pumpkin (squash)

100 g (3½ oz/½ cup) corn kernels

3 tablespoons diced, roasted and peeled red capsicum (pepper)

25 g (1 oz) reduced-fat feta cheese, grated

2 asparagus spears, finely chopped

1 tablespoon snipped chives

3 eggs and 3 egg whites, lightly beaten

Preheat the oven to 160ºC (315ºF/Gas 2–3). Line four 10 cm (4 inch) tart tins with the pastry, tucking the corners under neatly.

Layer the pumpkin, corn, capsicum, feta, asparagus and chives in the tins. Gently pour the beaten egg over the top. Bake for about 45 minutes, or until set.

Serves 4

Nutrition per serve: Energy: 702 kJ (168 Cals); Protein: 12 g; Total fat: 5 g; Carbohydrate: 17 g; Fibre: 2 g; Sodium: 221 mg

picnic prawn and pesto wraps

nori cornets filled with salmon sashimi

330 g (11¾ oz/1½ cups) white short-grain rice

3 tablespoons mirin

2 teaspoons brown rice vinegar

2 nori sheets

1 small avocado, sliced

¼ small cucumber, cut into 8 strips

¼ red capsicum (pepper), cut into 8 strips

200 g (7 oz) salmon fillet, cut into 8 strips

¼ teaspoon wasabi paste

2 teaspoons tamari soy sauce

1 teaspoon pickled ginger

Put the rice in a saucepan and cover with about 750 ml (26 fl oz/3 cups) of water. Bring to the boil, reduce the heat and simmer for 15 minutes. Turn out into a shallow dish and pour the mirin and vinegar over the top. Leave to cool.

Cut each nori sheet into quarters. Place a small amount of rice diagonally across the centre of the square of nori. Top with a slice each of avocado, cucumber, capsicum and salmon and then roll the nori up into a cone to enclose the filling. The filling will poke out of the top of the cornet.

Put the wasabi, soy sauce and pickled ginger in separate small bowls and serve with the cornets.

Serves 4

Nutrition per serve: Energy: 1808 kJ (432 Cals); Protein: 17 g; Total fat: 11 g; Carbohydrate: 66 g; Fibre: 3 g; Sodium: 259 mg

stir-fried salmon with sticky rice

500 g (1 lb 2 oz/2 cups) black sticky rice

½ teaspoon sesame oil

½ teaspoon minced garlic

½ teaspoon minced fresh ginger

1 onion, sliced

150 g (5½ oz) bok choy, Chinese cabbage or bean sprouts

125 ml (4 fl oz/½ cup) fish stock (page 171)

1 teaspoon tamari soy sauce

1 teaspoon sweet chilli sauce

1 teaspoon cornflour (cornstarch)

400 g (14 oz) salmon, boned and diced

1 teaspoon chopped fresh coriander (cilantro) leaves

Cook the black sticky rice according to the instructions on the packet.

Heat the oil in a wok or deep frying pan and add the garlic, ginger, onion and vegetables. Stir-fry for 1 minute.

Mix together the fish stock, soy sauce and sweet chilli sauce. Mix the cornflour with 3 teaspoons of water until smooth and add to the sauce. Add to the wok, bring to the boil and add the salmon. Cook for 3 minutes, stirring gently and then serve over the sticky rice. Garnish with the coriander.

Serves 4

Nutrition per serve: Energy: 1085 kJ (259 Cals); Protein: 22 g; Total fat: 8 g; Carbohydrate: 24 g; Fibre: 2 g; Sodium: 103 mg

sunset

sunset

Sunset is a special time of day and, while lunch might be a quick meal, the evening is when we have a tradition of sitting down to enjoy a more leisurely dinner. The evening meal might be something we've planned and quietly looked forward to during the afternoon: the focal point of our day. It can be a time to relax in the peace of our own company or sit down with family to talk over the day. It is often when we invite friends into our homes and create a special, more formal, dinner with a starter, main course and dessert. Many people mistakenly think it's impossible to do this while following principles of healthy eating, but our chefs have found it easy to prove them wrong.

The guidelines for creating a healthy evening meal are to make plant foods the major component (vegetables should make up about half of the meal), to include a nutritious carbohydrate and a serving of lean protein, and to minimize the oil used. We have also paid close attention to keeping sodium and fat to a minimum. Instead of heavily salting our meals, we emphasize the use of herbs, spices, garlic, onion, lemon juice, vinegar and home-made vegetable stock. These foods all add intense flavour, while being rich in healthy phytochemicals.

fresh vitality pure nourishing luscious healthy balance variety fresh vitality pure nourishing luscious healthy balance variety

asparagus and minted pea soup

2 small leeks, chopped

1 litre (35 fl oz/4 cups) vegetable stock (page 170)

1 teaspoon cumin

350 g (12 oz/2 bunches) asparagus, chopped

1 small head broccoli florets

3 tablespoons cashew nuts

155 g (5½ oz/1 cup) peas

fresh mint, to garnish

Sauté the leeks in a little of the stock with the cumin and some salt and pepper until the leeks are soft.

Add the asparagus, broccoli, cashew nuts and remaining stock and bring slowly to the boil. Reduce the heat and simmer for 15 minutes, then add the peas.

Transfer to a blender and blend until smooth. Reheat and garnish with mint leaves to serve.

Serves 12

Nutrition per serve: Energy: 148 kJ (35 Cals); Protein: 3 g; Total fat: 2 g; Carbohydrate: 3 g; Fibre: 2 g; Sodium: 57 mg

fettucine carbonara

200 g (7 oz) firm tofu, diced

2 tablespoons tamari soy sauce

300 g (10½ oz) fettucine

3 tablespoons lemon juice

300 g (10½ oz) button mushrooms, cut into quarters

6 large field mushrooms, whole

175 g (6 oz/1 bunch) asparagus spears, blanched and sliced diagonally

1 red capsicum (pepper), blanched and cut into strips

750 ml (26 fl oz/3 cups) white sauce (page 180), warmed

2 tablespoons snipped chives or basil leaves

Put the tofu on a paper-lined baking tray and sprinkle with the tamari, making sure the tofu is covered. Bake for 30 minutes or until firm, stirring occasionally so that the tofu cooks evenly.

Cook the pasta in a large pan of boiling water until *al dente*. Drain and set aside. Put a little of the lemon juice in a frying pan with a sprinkling of salt and pepper. Add the button mushrooms and cook until golden, adding more lemon juice if needed. Remove from the pan and cook the whole field mushrooms in the same way. Arrange one field mushroom on each serving plate.

Mix together the pasta, button mushrooms, tofu, asparagus and capsicum. Season with salt and pepper, add the white sauce and gently mix through to coat the pasta.

Spoon the pasta over the mushrooms and serve immediately, garnished with the chives or basil.

Serves 6

CHEF'S TIP: Those with a gluten intolerance can still enjoy this recipe by using gluten-free pasta.

Nutrition per serve: Energy: 1407 kJ (336 Cals); Protein: 19 g; Total fat: 8 g; Carbohydrate: 46 g; Fibre: 8 g; Sodium: 400 mg

pan-seared snapper
with a warm salad

juice of 1 lemon

100 ml (3½ fl oz) balsamic vinegar

1 red onion, sliced into fine wedges

4 roma (plum) tomatoes, roughly diced

6 mushrooms, sliced

1 zucchini (courgette), roughly diced

1 red capsicum (pepper), roasted, peeled and sliced

12 black olives

12 capers

fresh basil, chopped, plus a few sprigs to garnish

4 x 125 g (4½ oz) snapper fillets, bones and skin removed

150 g (5½ oz) rocket (arugula)

30 g (1 oz) reduced-fat feta cheese, grated

Put a splash of lemon juice and a splash of balsamic vinegar in a frying pan, add the onion and a sprinkle of salt and pepper. Cook for 30 seconds, add the tomatoes, mushrooms and zucchini and then continue cooking for 2–3 minutes. Add the capsicum, olives and capers and cook for 5 minutes until tender. Remove from the heat. Add the chopped basil and salt and pepper if needed.

Put a little more lemon juice and a sprinkle of salt and pepper in a hot frying pan, add the snapper and cook over high heat for 1 minute on each side. Turn off the heat, cover the pan and leave to stand for 5 minutes (the fish will complete its cooking in the hot pan).

Arrange a bed of rocket on each plate and serve the warm salad over the rocket, topped with a sprinkling of feta and a splash of balsamic vinegar. Place the fish on top and garnish with sprigs of basil.

Serves 4

Nutrition per serve: Energy: 916 kJ (219 Cals); Protein: 33 g; Total fat: 4 g; Carbohydrate: 10 g; Fibre: 5 g; Sodium: 308 mg

gado gado

150 g (5½ oz) firm tofu, cut into small strips

1½ tablespoons tamari soy sauce

90 g (3¼ oz/1 cup) bean sprouts, trimmed

1 red capsicum (pepper), julienned

3 tablespoons chopped fresh coriander (cilantro)

3 tablespoons chopped fresh basil

6 cherry tomatoes, chopped

4 baby corn spears, chopped

1 carrot, peeled and julienned

150 g (5½ oz) broccoli, cut into florets

150 g (5½ oz) cauliflower, cut into florets

8 asparagus spears, sliced diagonally

100 g (3½ oz) green beans, sliced diagonally

2 hard-boiled eggs, quartered

1 lime, cut into wedges

80–100 ml (about 3 fl oz) Balinese satay sauce (page 185)

Preheat the oven to 200°C (400°F/Gas 6). Put the tofu on a paper-lined baking tray and sprinkle with the tamari, making sure the tofu is covered. Bake for 30 minutes or until firm, stirring occasionally so that the tofu cooks evenly.

Mix together the bean sprouts, capsicum, coriander, basil and tomatoes. Cook the corn, carrot, broccoli, cauliflower, asparagus and beans in boiling water for 1 minute until just tender. Drain and refresh under cold water.

Arrange the salad and vegetables on a large platter, then top with boiled egg quarters and tofu strips. Garnish with lime wedges and serve with Balinese satay sauce and steamed rice.

Serves 4

Nutrition per serve: Energy: 633 kJ (151 Cals); Protein: 14 g; Total fat: 7 g; Carbohydrate: 8 g; Fibre: 6 g; Sodium: 457 mg

sweetcorn and lemon grass soup with coriander and coconut milk

3 corn cobs

2 leeks, white part only, chopped

2 lemon grass stalks, white part only, chopped

1½ litres (52 fl oz/6 cups) vegetable stock (page 170)

2 large carrots, peeled and diced

200 ml (7 fl oz) reduced-fat coconut milk

fresh coriander (cilantro), chopped, to garnish

Cut the corn kernels from the cobs and add the shaved cobs to your vegetable stock. In a large stockpot, sauté the leeks and lemon grass in a little of the stock for 5 minutes, seasoning with salt and pepper.

Add the carrots and corn kernels, cover the pan and cook for a further 10 minutes, or until the carrots are tender. Add more stock if necessary.

Top up with the remaining stock. Cover the pan again and bring to the boil. Reduce the heat and gently simmer for 30 minutes.

Leave to cool a little, then remove the shaved corn cobs and blend the soup until smooth. Pass the soup through a fine sieve and add the coconut milk. Reheat and serve with coriander sprinkled over the top.

Serves 8

CHEF'S TIP: Soup is great to make in large quantities. This one freezes well: for best results, blend it again after thawing.

Nutrition per serve: Energy: 341 kJ (82 Cals); Protein: 3 g; Total fat: 2 g; Carbohydrate: 12 g; Fibre: 4 g; Sodium: 131 mg

ocean trout with roma tomato and caper sauce and avocado mash

sauce

1 small red onion, chopped

1 tablespoon balsamic vinegar

10 roma (plum) tomatoes, roasted (page 113) and peeled

2 teaspoons small capers

1 teaspoon pine nuts

1 tablespoon chopped fresh basil

6 potatoes, peeled

2 garlic cloves, roasted (page 113) and peeled

60 ml (2 fl oz/¼ cup) white sauce (page 180)

¼ small avocado

3 tablespoons lemon juice

4 x125 g (4½ oz) pieces ocean trout

fresh basil sprigs, to garnish

To make the sauce, heat 1 tablespoon of water in a saucepan and sauté the red onion with a sprinkling of salt and pepper until soft. Add the balsamic vinegar and cook for 1 minute.

Add the roasted tomatoes, capers, pine nuts and 2 tablespoons of water and slowly bring to the boil. Reduce the heat and simmer gently for about 40 minutes until the sauce has thickened, stirring occasionally. Add the basil and more salt and pepper, if required.

Meanwhile, boil the potatoes in salted water for about 25 minutes, or until tender. Drain. Add the garlic and white sauce and mash well. Mash in the avocado.

Put the lemon juice in a frying pan over high heat, add the fish, season with salt and pepper and cook for 1 minute on each side. If the pan dries out, add a little water. Turn off the heat, cover the pan and leave for 5 minutes (the fish will complete its cooking in the pan).

Serve the fish on top of the mash, with the tomato sauce over the top. Garnish with basil sprigs.

Serves 4

Nutrition per serve: Energy: 1718 kJ (410 Cals); Protein: 35 g; Total fat: 14 g; Carbohydrate: 34 g; Fibre: 9 g; Sodium: 107 mg

beef and barley risotto

225 g (8 oz/1 cup) pearl barley
3 tablespoons white sauce (page 180)
1 teaspoon chopped fresh tarragon
250 ml (9 fl oz/1 cup) veal or beef stock
1 teaspoon cornflour (cornstarch)
8 spears baby corn, sliced lengthways
8 cherry tomatoes
8 English spinach leaves, trimmed
4 x 125 g (4½ oz) beef fillets
1 tablespoon mustard seed oil
½ teaspoon celery salt
½ teaspoon smoked paprika

Rinse the barley and then put in a large saucepan with 750 ml (26 fl oz/3 cups) of water. Simmer for 40 minutes, until the barley is soft and the water absorbed. Stir through the white sauce and tarragon and keep warm.

Meanwhile, put the stock in a pan and simmer until reduced by half. Mix the cornflour with 2 teaspoons of water until smooth and add to the stock. Stir until smooth.

Preheat the oven to 180°C (350°F/Gas 4). Put the corn on a paper-lined baking tray and roast for 10 minutes. Add the tomatoes to the tray for the last couple of minutes to warm through. Rinse the spinach and put in a pan with just the water clinging to its leaves. Cover the pan and wilt the spinach over low heat for 1 minute.

Brush the pieces of beef with the mustard seed oil and sprinkle with the combined celery salt and smoked paprika. Grill (broil) or pan-fry for about 4 minutes on each side, or to your taste.

Place a mound of barley risotto in the centre of each plate. Top with a piece of beef. Arrange the corn, tomatoes and spinach around the risotto. Spoon the sauce around the dish and serve immediately.

Serves 4

Nutrition per serve: Energy: 1640 kJ (391 Cals); Protein: 33 g; Total fat: 13 g; Carbohydrate: 35 g; Fibre: 8 g; Sodium: 127 mg

thai fish pie

1 tablespoon lemon juice

3 makrut (kaffir lime) leaves

800 g (1 lb 12 oz) boneless white fish, cut into strips

200 g (7 oz) button mushrooms, quartered

2 tablespoons tamari soy sauce

1 stalk lemon grass, white part only

3 coriander (cilantro) roots

400 ml (14 fl oz) reduced-fat coconut milk

1 cm (½ inch) piece of fresh ginger, chopped

2 tablespoons honey or maple syrup

1 garlic clove

1 red chilli

zest of 1 lime

1½ tablespoons cornflour (cornstarch)

125 g (4½ oz) baby spinach

4 asparagus spears, chopped

sweet potato mash (page 112)

Preheat the oven to 200°C (400°F/Gas 6). Blend the lemon juice and lime leaves together with a little water and a sprinkling of salt and pepper. Put in a bowl, add the fish and mix together with your hands to thoroughly coat the fish. Arrange the fish on a paper-lined baking tray and bake for 10 minutes. Remove from the oven and drain the fish through a colander, keeping the liquid.

Put the mushrooms on a paper-lined baking tray, sprinkle with tamari and bake for 15 minutes.

Put the lemon grass, coriander roots, coconut milk, ginger, honey, garlic, chilli, lime zest and reserved fish liquid in a blender and mix until smooth. Transfer to a pan and bring slowly to the boil. Mix the cornflour with 2 tablespoons of water and add to the pan. Stir until smooth and thickened.

Layer the spinach, asparagus, mushrooms and fish in a 3 litre (104 fl oz/12 cup) pie dish or four individual pie dishes. Cover with the sauce and spoon sweet potato mash over the top. Bake for 15 minutes.

Serves 4

Nutrition per serve: Energy: 1406 kJ (336 Cals); Protein: 31 g; Total fat: 6 g; Carbohydrate: 37 g; Fibre: 5 g; Sodium: 578 mg

sweet potato mash

2 orange sweet potatoes, approximately 1 kg (2 lb 4 oz)

125 ml (4 fl oz/½ cup) white sauce (page 180)

2 teaspoons snipped chives

Peel the sweet potatoes and put in a large saucepan. Cover with salted water and bring to the boil. Reduce the heat and simmer for about 30 minutes or until soft.

Drain the potatoes well and return them to the pan. Add the sauce and chives and mash thoroughly.

Delicious served as an accompaniment to fish.

Serves 6 as a side dish.

Nutrition per serve: Energy: 517 kJ (124 Cals); Protein: 4 g; Total fat: 1 g; Carbohydrate: 25 g; Fibre: 4 g; Sodium: 73 mg

roasted tomatoes, garlic and capsicum

6 roma (plum) tomatoes
1 garlic bulb (about 8 cloves)
1 red capsicum (pepper)
fresh rosemary or basil

Preheat the oven to 200°C (400°F/Gas 6). Trim the stalk ends from the tomatoes and then cut in half lengthways. Put the tomatoes, skin side up, on a baking tray, and bake for about 30 minutes. Leave to cool and then peel off the skin.

Put the garlic on a piece of foil, sprinkle with sea salt and pepper and then wrap up in the foil. Bake for 20–30 minutes (depending on the size of your garlic bulb).

Preheat the grill (broiler) to very hot. Cut the sides off the capsicum and put, skin side up, on a grill tray. Grill the capsicum until the skin blackens and blisters. Put the capsicum in a plastic bag and leave to cool. The skin will then be easy to peel away.

Gently mix together the tomatoes, garlic and pepper. Stir in a little chopped rosemary or basil and serve with steamed fish or chicken.

Serves 4

CHEF'S TIP: For variation, put some fresh herbs, such as rosemary, in the foil with the garlic before roasting.

Nutrition per serve: Energy: 189 kJ (45 Cals); Protein: 3 g; Total fat: 0 g; Carbohydrate: 6 g; Fibre: 4 g; Sodium: 16 mg

vegetable brochette with goat's cheese dressing and lentil casserole

2 tablespoons green lentils

2 teaspoons low-fat yoghurt

1 teaspoon chopped fresh dill

1 tomato, diced

50 g (1¾ oz) cucumber, peeled and diced

2 baby eggplants (aubergines), cut into quarters

1 small zucchini (courgette), cut into quarters

1 small red capsicum (pepper), cut into 8 pieces

1 small onion, cut into quarters

8 cherry tomatoes

4 button mushrooms

2 small yellow squash, halved

1 tablespoon goat's cheese

2 teaspoons chopped fresh coriander (cilantro)

1 teaspoon chopped fresh mint

2 tablespoons red capsicum sauce (page 181)

Put the lentils in a saucepan with 500 ml (17 fl oz/2 cups) of water and bring to the boil. Simmer for 30 minutes until soft then leave to cool. Add the yoghurt, dill, tomato and cucumber and mix together.

If you are using wooden skewers, soak them in water for a while to prevent scorching. Thread the eggplant, zucchini, capsicum, onion, cherry tomatoes, mushrooms and yellow squash onto long skewers. Place under a hot grill (broiler) or cook in a frying pan for 6 minutes.

Mix together the goat's cheese, coriander and mint.

Make a small lentil patty on each plate. Top with a mound of goat's cheese and serve with a skewer on the side. Drizzle a little red capsicum sauce around the plate before serving.

Serves 4 as a starter

Nutrition per serve: Energy: 373 kJ (89 Cals); Protein: 7 g; Total fat: 1 g; Carbohydrate: 12 g; Fibre: 6 g; Sodium: 73 mg

mexican chilli beans with guacamole and lavash chips

chilli beans

200 g (7 oz) kidney beans, soaked in water for 1 hour

1 large red onion, chopped

200 g (7 oz) pumpkin (squash), peeled, seeded and diced

1 teaspoon paprika

1 teaspoon cumin

1 teaspoon golden door chilli (page 180)

1 red capsicum (pepper), roasted, peeled and chopped (page 113)

1 kg (2 lb 4 oz) roma (plum) tomatoes, roasted and peeled (page 113)

2 tablespoons chopped fresh basil

to serve

2 sheets lavash bread

1 teaspoon paprika

¼ iceberg lettuce, shredded

1 carrot, grated

280 g (10 oz) low-fat cottage cheese

½ red onion, thinly sliced

4 tablespoons guacamole (page 184)

4 tablespoons golden door yoghurt (page 34)

To make the chilli beans, drain the kidney beans, put in a saucepan and cover with fresh water. Bring to the boil then reduce the heat to simmer for 40 minutes or until beans are tender. Drain and set aside.

Put the onion, pumpkin, spices and chilli in a saucepan with salt and pepper and 2 tablespoons of water. Sauté over medium heat for 5 minutes, then add the roasted capsicum and tomatoes and cover the pan. Cook, stirring occasionally for 25 minutes. Add the beans and basil and cook for another 5 minutes.

Preheat the oven to 200°C (400°F/Gas 6). Cut the lavash bread into triangles, sprinkle with the paprika and place on a paper-lined baking tray. Bake for about 3 minutes or until crisp.

Serve the chilli beans in individual dishes. Arrange a layer of lettuce in the base of each dish, then a layer of carrot, beans, cottage cheese, red onion, another layer of lettuce, carrot, more beans and cheese. Top with 1 tablespoon of guacamole. Serve with the lavash chips and yoghurt.

Serves 4

CHEF'S NOTE: Any leftover chilli beans can be stored in an airtight container in the fridge for up to 4 days.

Nutrition per serve: Energy: 1562 kJ (373 Cals); Protein: 33 g; Total fat: 6 g; Carbohydrate: 47 g; Fibre: 15 g; Sodium: 361 mg

lemon grass and turmeric fish

1 tablespoon Indian mustard seeds

2 teaspoons garam masala

1 tablespoon turmeric powder

2.5 cm (1 inch) piece of fresh ginger

3 lemon grass stalks, white part only

1 garlic clove, chopped

3 coriander (cilantro) roots and stems

1 onion, sliced

1 red capsicum (pepper), sliced

½ teaspoon golden door chilli (page 180)

200 ml (7 fl oz) reduced-fat coconut milk

800 g (1 lb 12 oz) boneless white fish, cut into strips

lime, mango and mint couscous (page 87), to serve

coriander (cilantro) sprigs, to garnish

Heat a frying pan and dry-fry the mustard seeds, garam masala and turmeric for 1–2 minutes until fragrant. Mix the ginger, lemon grass, garlic and coriander with a little water in a mortar and pestle until a fine paste forms.

Add the onion, capsicum, chilli and paste to the spices in the pan. Add a little water and fry gently for 10 minutes until the onion is soft. Season and leave to cool.

Stir together the coconut milk and spice paste and add the fish pieces. Leave to marinate for 30 minutes. Preheat the oven to 200°C (400°F/Gas 6). Spread the fish on a paper-lined baking tray and bake for 10 minutes until cooked through. Serve with the couscous and sprigs of coriander.

Serves 4

CHEF'S TIP: To reduce the fat quantity of this dish, use low-fat yoghurt instead of coconut milk.

Nutrition per serve: Energy: 1679 kJ (401 Cals); Protein: 45 g; Total fat: 5 g; Carbohydrate: 42 g; Fibre: 2 g; Sodium: 227 mg

pumpkin, spinach and tofu lasagne

4 wholemeal lasagne sheets

40 g (1½ oz/½ cup) fresh white breadcrumbs

4 slices eggplant (aubergine)

250 ml (9 fl oz/1 cup) white sauce (page 180)

4 tablespoons reduced-fat ricotta cheese

pinch of smoked paprika

240 g (9 oz) firm tofu, sliced

70 g (2½ oz/2 cups) chopped English spinach

2 tablespoons diced onion

1 garlic clove, minced

1 tomato, chopped

600 g (1 lb 5 oz) pumpkin (squash), peeled, cooked and mashed

500 ml (17 fl oz/2 cups) tomato pasta sauce (page 179)

100 g (3½ oz) zucchini (courgette), sliced lengthways

Preheat the oven to 180°C (350°F/Gas 4). Cook the pasta sheets for 5 minutes in boiling water and then drain on a tea towel or paper towels.

Spread the breadcrumbs on a baking tray and toast in the oven for 5 minutes until lightly golden and crisp.

Lightly spray the eggplant slices with oil and grill (broil) or pan-fry, turning once, until softened.

Mix together half the white sauce with the ricotta, paprika and tofu slices and spread over the base of a 3 litre (104 fl oz/12 cup) casserole dish. Spread the spinach over the sauce. Lay two of the lasagne sheets over the top. Layer the eggplant slices, onion, garlic, tomato, pumpkin mash and half the tomato sauce over the top. Lay another two lasagne sheets on top. Spread the remaining white sauce, the zucchini slices and remaining tomato sauce over the top. Sprinkle with the breadcrumbs and bake for 20 minutes. Allow to stand for 5 minutes before serving.

Serves 4

CHEF'S TIP: Those with a gluten intolerance can still enjoy this recipe by using gluten-free pasta.

Nutrition per serve: Energy: 1428 kJ (341 Cals); Protein: 21 g; Total fat: 11 g; Carbohydrate: 39 g; Fibre: 10 g; Sodium: 205 mg

tuscan roast vegetables

2 parsnips, peeled and diced

2 carrots, peeled and diced

2 red or yellow capsicums (peppers), chopped

500 g (1 lb 2 oz) field or Swiss brown mushrooms, cut into halves or quarters

2 zucchini (courgettes), peeled and diced

2 garlic cloves, chopped

1 tablespoon chopped fresh rosemary

1 tablespoon chopped fresh basil

1 tablespoon chopped fresh flat-leaf (Italian) parsley

60 g (2¼ oz/½ cup) kalamata olives with their liquid

Preheat the oven to 220°C (425°F/Gas 7). Gently mix together the parsnips, carrots, capsicum, mushrooms, zucchini, garlic and rosemary in a large bowl.

Arrange the parsnips and carrots around the edge of a paper-lined baking tray and the capsicum, mushrooms and zucchini in the middle. Bake for about 30 minutes or until tender.

Put the roasted vegetables in a large serving bowl. Add the basil, parsley, olives and olive liquid and mix together thoroughly before serving.

Serves 6 as a side dish

Nutrition per serve: Energy: 290 kJ (69 cal); Protein: 5 g; Total fat: 1 g; Carbohydrate: 10 g; Fibre: 5 g; Sodium: 89 mg

chicken with mushroom quinoa

100 g (3½ oz/½ cup) quinoa

4 x 125 g (4½ oz) chicken breasts, skin removed

½ teaspoon salt and smoked paprika mix

¼ teaspoon mustard seed oil

1 teaspoon mustard seeds

½ small onion, chopped

45 g (1¾ oz/½ cup) chopped mixed mushrooms

125 ml (4 fl oz/½ cup) chicken stock

juice of 4 apples (about 375 ml/1½ cups)

2 teaspoons balsamic vinegar

2 vine-ripened tomatoes, diced

2 teaspoons chopped fresh parsley

zest and juice of 1 lemon

Wash the quinoa in plenty of cold water and drain. Put in a pan with 250 ml (9 fl oz/1 cup) of water. Bring to the boil and then reduce the heat, cover the pan and simmer for 10–12 minutes until all the water has been absorbed.

Preheat the oven to 180°C (350°F/Gas 4). Sprinkle the chicken breasts with the paprika seasoning. Heat a non-stick frying pan and add the chicken to the dry pan. Cook for 2 minutes to sear, then turn over and sear the other side. Transfer the chicken to a paper-lined baking tray and bake for 12 minutes.

Put the mustard seed oil in a saucepan over low heat. Add the mustard seeds. Add the onion and fry for 5 minutes, until lightly golden. Add the mushrooms and stock and cook until the stock has reduced by half.

Add the apple juice and cook for 15 minutes until reduced by half. Add the vinegar, season with salt and pepper and stir in the quinoa.

Toss together the tomatoes, parsley, lemon zest and juice. Serve the quinoa topped with the chicken and the tomato salad.

Serves 4

Nutrition per serve: Energy: 1347 kJ (322 Cals); Protein: 32 g; Total fat: 9 g; Carbohydrate: 27 g; Fibre: 4 g; Sodium: 95 mg

smoked salmon lasagne with vine-ripened tomato salad

white sauce

500 g (1 lb 2 oz) leeks, white part only, chopped

50 g (1¾ oz) cashew nuts

400 ml (14 fl oz) low-fat soy milk

1½ teaspoons cornflour (cornstarch)

filling

200 g (7 oz) baby button mushrooms, sliced

2 tablespoons balsamic vinegar

2 tablespoons chopped fresh basil

150 g (6 sheets) fresh egg lasagne

150 g (5½ oz) baby spinach

150 g (5½ oz) asparagus spears, chopped (keep the tips for the salad)

100 g (3½ oz) smoked salmon

25 g (1 oz) anchovy fillets, soaked in milk and then finely diced

50 g (1¾ oz) low-fat feta cheese, crumbled

tomato salad

250 g (9 oz) small vine-ripened tomatoes, halved

1 tablespoon chopped fresh lemon thyme

1 tablespoon balsamic vinegar

Preheat the oven to 180°C (350°F/Gas 4). To make the white sauce, sauté the leeks and cashew nuts in a little water until soft. Transfer to a blender and add the milk. Blend until smooth and then return to the pan.

Mix the cornflour with 2 teaspoons of water until smooth, and then add to the sauce. Bring back to the boil. If the sauce seems too thick, add more milk. If too thin, add more cornflour. Season with salt and pepper.

Put the mushrooms and balsamic vinegar in a frying pan and cook over high heat, stirring occasionally, for 5 minutes. Remove from the heat and stir in the basil.

Spread a third of the white sauce over the base of a 3 litre (104 fl oz/12 cup) casserole dish. Add a layer of lasagne sheets, then half the spinach and the mushrooms. Top with another layer of lasagne, another third of the white sauce, the asparagus, salmon, anchovies, remaining spinach and then a final layer of pasta and sauce. Sprinkle the feta over the top. Cover and bake for 20 minutes, then uncover and grill (broil) for 5–8 minutes to brown the top.

To make the tomato salad, put the tomatoes and herbs on a paper-lined baking tray and sprinkle with the balsamic vinegar. Bake at 200°C (400°F/Gas 6) for 10 minutes, then mix with the asparagus tips and serve with the lasagne.

Serves 6

Nutrition per serve: Energy: 1493 kJ (356 Cals); Protein: 26 g; Total fat: 11 g; Carbohydrate: 36 g; Fibre: 10 g; Sodium: 990 mg

beef tenderloin with pumpkin relish and corn jus

pumpkin relish

½ teaspoon fennel seeds

½ teaspoon onion seeds (nigella)

½ teaspoon yellow mustard seeds

½ teaspoon fenugreek seeds

350 g (12 oz) pumpkin (squash), peeled, seeded and diced

1 small onion, finely chopped

2 tablespoons white wine vinegar

1 teaspoon caster (superfine) sugar

1 tablespoon sweet chilli sauce

20 g green peppercorns, rinsed and lightly crushed

kernels cut from 2 corn cobs

250 ml (9 fl oz/1 cup) chicken stock

4 x 125 g (4½ oz) beef tenderloin fillets

1 teaspoon mustard seed oil

½ teaspoon smoked paprika

185 g (6½ oz/1 cup) cooked brown rice

185 g (6½ oz/1 cup) cooked white rice

4 tablespoons cooked black rice

To make the relish, put the seeds in a non-stick frying pan and dry-fry until aromatic. Remove from the pan. Add a splash of water to the pan and fry the pumpkin gently for 3–4 minutes. Add the onion, seeds, vinegar and sugar and cook, stirring occasionally for 5 minutes. Add the chilli sauce and peppercorns. Cook for 2 minutes, then season with salt and set aside.

To roast the corn, preheat the oven to 200°C (400°F/ Gas 6). Spread the kernels on a paper-lined baking tray. Roast for 20 minutes until dried out a little. Put in a food processor with the chicken stock and purée until smooth.

To cook the beef, pat dry with paper towels. Brush with the oil, sprinkle with paprika and pan-fry the steaks in a hot non-stick frying pan for 2–3 minutes on each side or until cooked to your taste.

Mix together the three different rices and arrange on the serving plates. Serve the steak on the rice with a spoonful of relish and a little corn jus drizzled around.

Serves 4

CHEF'S TIP: You will need to cook about ⅓ cup of brown or white rice to produce 1 cup of cooked rice.

Nutrition per serve: Energy: 1645 kJ (393 Cals); Protein: 31 g; Total fat: 8 g; Carbohydrate: 47g; Fibre: 3 g; Sodium: 242 mg

potato and rocket salad
with dijon vinaigrette

750 g (1 lb 10 oz) unpeeled kipfler potatoes, halved if large

120 g (4½ oz) rocket (arugula)

1 small red onion, finely sliced

1 red capsicum (pepper), roasted (page 113), peeled and cut into strips

8 sliced kalamata olives

½ teaspoon chopped fresh dill

4 hard-boiled eggs, cut into quarters

dressing

125 g (4½ oz/½ cup) dijon mustard

125 ml (4 fl oz/½ cup) apple juice concentrate

3 tablespoons lemon juice

3 tablespoons white balsamic vinegar

4 roasted garlic cloves (page 113), peeled

2 tablespoons roasted cashew nuts

Cook the potatoes in boiling salted water for 20 minutes until just tender. Drain and leave to cool.

Put the potatoes in a large salad bowl with the rocket, onion, capsicum, olives and dill. Toss together and season with salt and pepper.

To make the dressing, whisk together the mustard, apple concentrate, lemon juice, vinegar, garlic and cashews. Drizzle 1 tablespoon per person over the salad and arrange the eggs over the top.

Serves 4

CHEF'S TIP: The leftover dressing will keep in an airtight container in the fridge for 2 weeks.

Nutrition per serve: Energy: 1071 kJ (256 Cals); Protein: 14 g; Total fat: 7 g; Carbohydrate: 33 g; Fibre: 5 g; Sodium: 205 mg

dukka-coated chicken with roast lemons

4 x 125 g (4½ oz) chicken breasts (without skin)
60 g (2¼ oz) dukka (page 179)
2 lemons, halved

Preheat the oven to 180°C (350°F/Gas 4). Coat the top of each chicken breast with dukka. Heat a frying pan with an ovenproof handle and oil very lightly. Sear the chicken, dukka-side-down, in the pan for 1 minute and then turn the chicken over and transfer the pan to the oven.

Roast the chicken for 6 minutes, then add the lemon halves to the pan and roast for another 6 minutes.

Serves 4

Nutrition per serve: Energy: 897 kJ (214 Cals); Protein: 28 g; Total fat: 10 g; Carbohydrate: 2 g; Fibre: 2 g; Sodium: 249 mg

chicken stracciatella with parsley and pine nuts

60 g (2¼ oz) chicken breast
2 eggs
2 teaspoons grated parmesan cheese
2 teaspoons pine nuts
2 tablespoons chopped fresh parsley
800 ml (28 fl oz) chicken stock

Mince the chicken breast. Add the eggs, parmesan, pine nuts and parsley and blend together.

Put the stock in a pan and bring to the boil. Slowly pour the egg mixture into the boiling stock. Season well and bring back to the boil before serving.

Serves 4 as a starter

Nutrition per serve: Energy: 251 kJ (60 Cals); Protein: 7 g; Total fat: 4 g; Carbohydrate: 0 g; Fibre: 0 g; Sodium: 56 mg

tofu and shiitake spring rolls with herb and sesame dipping sauce

spring rolls

250 g (9 oz) firm tofu

3 tablespoons tamari soy sauce

300 g (10½ oz) Chinese cabbage, shredded

zest and juice of 1 lime

200 g (7 oz) bean sprouts

1 onion, finely diced

3 garlic cloves, finely chopped

1 teaspoon finely chopped chilli

1 tablespoon finely chopped lemon grass, white part only

1½ teaspoons Chinese five-spice

150 g (5½ oz) shiitake mushrooms, sliced

3 tablespoons peanut butter

3 tablespoons chopped fresh coriander (cilantro)

about 20 spring roll wrappers

1 egg white, lightly beaten

dipping sauce

zest and juice of 2 limes

100 ml (3½ fl oz) ponzu sauce

3 tablespoons apple juice concentrate (or honey or maple syrup)

1 tablespoon finely chopped fresh mint

1 tablespoon finely chopped fresh coriander (cilantro)

1 tablespoon toasted sesame seeds

1 tablespoon finely chopped chilli

Preheat the oven to 200°C (400°F/Gas 6). Crumble the tofu onto a paper-lined baking tray and sprinkle with the tamari, making sure the tofu is covered. Bake for 15 minutes or until firm, stirring occasionally so that the tofu cooks evenly. Cool slightly. Put the Chinese cabbage, lime zest, bean sprouts and baked tofu in a mixing bowl and toss together gently.

Sauté the onion, garlic, chilli and lemon grass in a saucepan with a little water for 3 minutes. Season with salt and pepper and add the five-spice and shiitake mushrooms. Cook for another 2 minutes (if the pan dries out add a little more water). Add the peanut butter, coriander and lime juice and mix together thoroughly. Leave to cool. Combine with the cabbage mixture.

Place a spring roll wrapper on a dry work surface in a diamond shape. Place ½ cup of filling on the bottom corner of the diamond and fold the corner of the wrapper up over it. Roll halfway up, then fold in the left and right sides and roll up to the top. Do the same with the remaining wrappers and filling. Increase the oven to 220°C (425°F/Gas 7). Put the spring rolls on a paper-lined baking tray, brush with egg white and bake for 10 minutes until golden.

To make the dipping sauce, whisk together all the ingredients. Serve with the spring rolls.

Makes about 20 rolls

Nutrition per roll: Energy: 424 kJ (101 Cals); Protein: 6 g;
Total fat: 4 g; Carbohydrate: 11 g; Fibre: 2 g; Sodium: 269 mg

thai green curry fish

green curry sauce

250 g (9 oz) leeks, white part only, chopped

200 g (7 oz) pumpkin (squash), diced

1 clove roasted garlic (page 113)

30 g (1 oz) cashew nuts

¼ teaspoon trocomare (herb salt)

1½ teaspoons Thai green curry paste

500 ml (17 fl oz/2 cups) soy milk

300 g (10½ oz) firm fish fillets (eg salmon), cut into large chunks

1 tablespoon lime juice

150 g (5½ oz) button mushrooms, sliced

1 onion, cut into thin wedges

1 fennel bulb, cut into thin wedges

½ teaspoon trocomare (herb salt)

1 tablespoon lime juice

100 g (3½ oz) baby spinach

4 asparagus spears, blanched and sliced diagonally

2 tablespoons chopped fresh basil

lime wedges and fresh coriander (cilantro) sprigs, to garnish

Put the leeks, pumpkin, garlic, cashews, trocomare and curry paste in a saucepan with 2 tablespoons of water and sauté for 10 minutes, until the pumpkin and leeks are soft. Add the soy milk and transfer to a blender. Blend until the sauce is smooth.

Preheat the oven to 200°C (400°F/Gas 6). Put the fish on a paper-lined baking tray and sprinkle with the lime juice and salt and pepper. Bake for 5 minutes, until the fish is cooked through. Drain off the excess liquid.

Put the mushrooms, onion, fennel, trocomare and lime juice on a paper-lined baking tray and bake for 20 minutes, until the vegetables are tender. Combine with the spinach, asparagus and basil. Add to the sauce and reheat gently. Add the fish and serve with rice or noodles, garnished with lime wedges and fresh coriander.

Serves 4

CHEF'S TIP: You can keep the liquid that you drain from the fish, freeze it and use as the base for stock or soup. For a vegetarian meal, use chickpeas instead of the fish.

Nutrition per serve: Energy: 1174 kJ (280 Cals); Protein: 26 g; Total fat: 11 g; Carbohydrate: 19 g; Fibre: 8 g; Sodium: 192 mg

lobster with risotto and mussel sauce

½ teaspoon mild mustard seed oil

½ onion, chopped

2 garlic cloves, crushed

4 button mushrooms, chopped

¼ red capsicum (pepper), diced

220 g (7 oz/1 cup) arborio rice

580 ml (20¼ fl oz/2⅓ cups) hot vegetable stock (page 170)

30 ml (1 fl oz) verjuice

½ teaspoon celery salt

½ tomato, chopped

12 baby spinach leaves

1 tablespoon chopped fresh parsley or basil

2 fresh lobsters, halved, heads and legs removed (your fishmonger will do this)

½ teaspoon olive oil

pinch of smoked paprika

pinch of celery salt

1 tablespoon chopped onion

2 teaspoons verjuice

2 tablespoons fish stock (page 171)

1 star anise

⅛ teaspoon lemon zest

4 fresh black mussels

½ teaspoon cornflour (cornstarch)

1 teaspoon chopped mixed herbs

1 tablespoon diced tomato

4 scallops

10 English spinach leaves

Heat the mustard seed oil in a large heavy-based saucepan. Add the onion and cook for 3 minutes until just softened. Add the garlic, mushrooms and capsicum and cook for 2 minutes. Add the rice and stir to coat well. Add a ladleful of stock and the verjuice and stir until absorbed. Add the celery salt and another ladleful of stock and stir until absorbed. Continue stirring for about 25 minutes, adding the stock slowly until it has all been absorbed and the rice is cooked. Add the tomato, spinach and herbs.

Meanwhile, preheat the oven to 180°C (350°F/Gas 4). Preheat a frying pan with an ovenproof handle. Brush the lobsters with olive oil and sprinkle with paprika and celery salt. Put in the pan and bake in the oven for 8 minutes.

Heat a heavy-based saucepan and add the onion, verjuice, stock, star anise, lemon zest and mussels. Cover the pan and cook for 1–2 minutes until the mussels open (discard any mussels that haven't opened). Mix the cornflour with 2 teaspoons of water until smooth and add to the pan. Stir over the heat until smooth and thickened. Add the herbs and tomato.

Put the scallops on a baking tray in the hot oven for 2 minutes. Wash the spinach leaves and put in a pan with just the water clinging to the leaves. Cover and cook for 30 seconds until wilted. Arrange the spinach on plates, with a scallop for each person. Add a spoonful of risotto and half a lobster and spoon the mussel sauce around.

Serves 4

Nutrition per serve: Energy: 1605 kJ (383 Cals); Protein: 42 g; Total fat: 3 g; Carbohydrate: 45 g; Fibre: 3 g; Sodium: 737 mg

ocean trout stir-fry with udon noodles and chilli lime sauce

4 x 125 g (4½ oz) pieces ocean trout

1 tablespoon lime juice

50 g (1¾ oz) dried udon noodles

1 carrot, julienned

1 red capsicum (pepper), julienned

4 spring onions (scallions), sliced diagonally

8 shiitake mushrooms, sliced

4 asparagus spears, sliced diagonally

1 bunch bok choy, shredded

3 tablespoons chopped fresh coriander (cilantro)

lime wedges and coriander (cilantro) sprigs, to garnish

sauce

juice of 1 lime

2 tablespoons fish sauce

3 tablespoons tamari soy sauce

1 tablespoon pure maple syrup

1 teaspoon grated or finely chopped fresh ginger

½ teaspoon finely chopped chilli

2 makrut (kaffir lime) leaves, shredded

Preheat the oven to 200°C (400°F/Gas 6). Put the fish on a paper-lined baking tray, drizzle with the lime juice and sprinkle with salt and pepper. Bake for 8 minutes, then remove from the oven and leave to stand for 3 minutes.

Meanwhile, cook the noodles according to the packet instructions and then drain. Make the sauce by mixing together all the ingredients in a bowl.

Put 2 tablespoons of water in a hot wok, then add the carrot and stir-fry for 1 minute. Add the capsicum, spring onions, mushrooms and asparagus and stir-fry for 2 minutes. (If the wok starts to dry, add a little bit more water.) Turn off the heat and add the bok choy, coriander, noodles and sauce. Toss together well.

Serve the fish on a bed of noodles, garnished with lime wedges and coriander.

Serves 4

CHEF'S TIP: This dish is relatively high in sodium. Those who wish to minimize their sodium intake could reduce the amount of fish sauce and soy sauce used.

A hot wok is essential for stir-frying. Don't add too much liquid at once or you will lower the cooking temperature and steam the food rather than stir-fry.

Nutrition per serve: Energy: 1018 kJ (243 Cals); Protein: 31 g; Total fat: 5 g; Carbohydrate: 17 g; Fibre: 3 g; Sodium: 1548 mg

teriyaki beef with cannellini bean purée

85 g (3 oz) dried cannellini beans
1 tablespoon wholegrain mustard
1 garlic clove, crushed
1 teaspoon chopped pickled ginger
2 tablespoons tamari soy sauce
4 x 125 g (4½ oz) beef fillets
8 asparagus spears
350 g (12 oz) cherry tomatoes
8 mushrooms
250 ml (9 fl oz/1 cup) beef or veal stock
3 tablespoons verjuice
2 teaspoons balsamic vinegar
½ teaspoon cornflour (cornstarch)

Put the beans in a pan and cover with cold water. Bring to the boil and boil for 5 minutes, remove from the heat and soak for 45 minutes. Drain and cover with cold water. Bring to the boil again, cover and simmer for 45 minutes until tender. Put in a blender with the mustard and 2–3 tablespoons of cooking water and mix until smooth.

Mix together the garlic, ginger and soy sauce. Add the beef and leave to marinate for 30 minutes. Preheat the oven to 200°C (400°F/Gas 6). Put the beef in a frying pan with an ovenproof handle and pan-fry over high heat until browned on both sides. Put the pan in the oven for 5 minutes or until the beef is cooked to your taste.

Blanch the asparagus in boiling water for 2 minutes and then refresh in cold water. Put the tomatoes on a baking tray and roast in the oven for 5 minutes. Sauté the mushrooms in a non-stick pan lightly sprayed with oil.

Put the stock, verjuice and vinegar in a saucepan and bring to the boil. Reduce the heat and simmer until reduced by half. Mix the cornflour with a little water until smooth and then whisk into the sauce. Bring back to the boil and remove from the heat.

Arrange the beef on a mound of bean purée, with the asparagus, tomatoes and mushrooms to the side. Pour a little sauce around before serving.

Serves 4

Nutrition per serve: Energy: 1118 kJ (267 Cals); Protein: 36 g; Total fat: 7 g; Carbohydrate: 15 g; Fibre: 7 g; Sodium: 506 mg

middle-eastern minted onion soup

4 large onions, thinly sliced

1 teaspoon maple syrup

½ teaspoon ground turmeric

pinch of ground cinnamon

pinch of ground cardamom

1 litre (35 fl oz/4 cups) vegetable stock (page 170)

2 tablespoons spelt flour, sieved

3 tablespoons lemon juice

2 tablespoons lime juice

2 tablespoons chopped fresh mint

Put the onion, maple syrup, spices, 5 tablespoons of the stock and a pinch of salt and pepper in a large heavy-based saucepan. Cover and cook over medium heat for 10–15 minutes, stirring occasionally, until the liquid has evaporated and the onions are caramelized and golden brown. Add a little water if the pan starts to dry out.

Stir in the flour and cook over low heat for 2 minutes. Gradually add the stock, a little at a time, stirring until the soup comes to the boil. Reduce the heat and simmer for 30 minutes.

Mix together the lemon and lime juice and add to the soup gradually, to your taste. Simmer for 5 more minutes, then stir in the mint and serve immediately.

Serves 10 as a starter

CHEF'S TIP: Soup is wonderful to make in bulk and freeze. If you are doing so, add the mint after thawing to prevent it discolouring.

Nutrition per serve: Energy: 135 kJ (32 Cals); Protein: 1 g; Total fat: 0 g; Carbohydrate: 6 g; Fibre: 1 g; Sodium: 130 mg

tofu curry with fragrant basmati rice

curry sauce

1 onion, diced

1 teaspoon cumin

1 teaspoon paprika

1½ teaspoon mild curry powder

2 tablespoons maple syrup

3 tablespoons chopped fresh coriander (cilantro)

200 ml (7 fl oz) reduced-fat coconut milk

1 cm (½ inch) piece of fresh ginger

1 garlic clove

juice of ½ lime

½ teaspoon chopped chilli

200 ml (7 fl oz) white sauce (page 180)

200 g (7 oz/1 cup) basmati rice

¼ teaspoon sea salt

3 makrut (kaffir lime) leaves

1 lemon grass stalk, lightly crushed

300 g (10½ oz) firm tofu, cut into strips

3 tablespoons tamari soy sauce

1 onion, sliced

1 carrot, julienned

100 g (3½ oz) green beans, sliced diagonally

115 g (4 oz) baby corn

1 red capsicum (pepper), sliced

1 bunch bok choy, chopped

To make the sauce, put the onion, spices and maple syrup in a pan with salt and pepper and 4 tablespoons of water and sauté for 2 minutes until the onion is tender. Add the coriander and cook over low heat for another minute.

Put the coconut milk, ginger, garlic, lime juice and chilli in a blender and mix for 30 seconds, then add to the pan. Cook for 2 minutes, then add the white sauce and cook for 20 minutes over low heat. Check the seasoning.

Wash the rice in a sieve and then put in a saucepan. Add 1.25 litres (44 fl oz/5 cups) cold water and add the salt, lime leaves and lemon grass. Boil for 12–15 minutes or until the rice is soft and fluffy. Rinse with boiling water.

Preheat the oven to 200°C (400°F/Gas 6). Put the tofu on a paper-lined baking tray and sprinkle with the tamari, making sure the tofu is covered. Bake for 15 minutes or until firm, stirring occasionally so that it cooks evenly.

Heat a wok and add a splash of water. Stir-fry the onion for 1 minute, then add the carrot, beans and corn and cook for 2–3 minutes. If the wok dries out, add another splash of water. Add the capsicum, bok choy and baked tofu and cook for 1 minute. Serve with the fragrant rice and curry sauce.

Serves 4

Nutrition per serve: Energy: 1851 kJ (442 Cals); Protein: 18 g; Total fat: 11 g; Carbohydrate: 67 g; Fibre: 7 g; Sodium: 758 mg

lemon myrtle chicken with sweet potato and ricotta tarts

4 x 125 g (4½ oz) chicken breasts

½ teaspoon lemon myrtle powder

3 French shallots, cut into quarters

250 g (9 oz/1 cup) low-fat yoghurt

¼ teaspoon turmeric

¼ teaspoon ground coriander

1 tablespoon verjuice

4 sheets filo pastry

450 g (1 lb) sweet potato, peeled and diced

80 g (2¾ oz/⅓ cup) low-fat ricotta cheese

80 g (2¾ oz/1 cup) chopped English spinach

Preheat the oven to 180°C (350°F/Gas 4). Coat the chicken with the lemon myrtle. Heat a frying pan with an oven-proof handle, spray with a little oil and add the chicken breasts. Cook for 1 minute to sear, then turn over and cook for 1 minute on the other side. Add the shallots and put in the oven for 6 minutes.

Mix together the yoghurt, turmeric, coriander and verjuice and pour over the chicken. Return to the oven for another 6 minutes.

Meanwhile, put the sweet potato on a paper-lined baking tray and roast for 15 minutes. Mix with the ricotta cheese and spinach.

Fold each filo sheet in half and then in half again. Use to line four 250 ml (9 fl oz/1 cup) non-stick muffin tins. Lightly spray with oil and bake for 6 minutes until golden brown. Spoon the sweet potato filling into the filo cases and serve with the chicken and shallots. Spoon a little of the chicken pan juices over each serving.

Serves 4

CHEF'S TIP: If you can't find lemon myrtle, you can mix finely grated lemon zest with chopped spring onion.

Nutrition per serve: Energy: 1426 kJ (341 Cals); Protein: 36 g; Total fat: 9 g; Carbohydrate: 28 g; Fibre: 3 g; Sodium: 280 mg

spicy couscous frittata with tomato and fennel

1 teaspoon coriander seeds

1 teaspoon cumin seeds

1 teaspoon black mustard seeds

1 teaspoon Moroccan spice

2 small red onions, finely sliced

6 mushrooms, finely sliced

8 sun-dried tomatoes (not in oil), chopped

1 zucchini (courgette), finely chopped

1 celery stalk, finely chopped

2 tablespoons chopped fresh coriander (cilantro)

1 garlic clove, chopped

250 ml (9 fl oz/1 cup) vegetable stock (page 170) or water

185 g (6½ oz/1 cup) couscous

tomato and fennel topping

200 g (7 oz) cherry tomatoes, quartered

½ head of fennel, finely sliced

½ teaspoon chopped fresh mint

omelette

6 egg whites and 2 yolks

1 tablespoon snipped chives

1 tablespoon skim milk

Put the seeds in a frying pan and toast over high heat until aromatic, taking care not to burn. Transfer to a mortar and pestle and grind the seeds with the Moroccan spice.

Put the onion, mushrooms, tomatoes, zucchini, celery, coriander, garlic and ground seeds in a saucepan with a little water and sauté until soft. Put the stock in a pan and bring to the boil. Remove from the heat and add the couscous. Stir, cover and leave for 3 minutes. Fluff with a fork and mix with the vegetables.

To make the tomato and fennel topping, put the cherry tomatoes and fennel in a saucepan with salt and pepper and a splash of water. Fry for about 3 minutes until tender. Add the mint and remove from the heat.

To make the omelette, mix together the egg, chives and milk and season with salt and pepper. Lightly spray an 18 cm (7 inch) non-stick frying pan with oil and pour in a third of the mixture. Cook over medium heat for 30 seconds, until the bottom has set, then turn and cook the other side. Make two more omelettes in the same way.

Place one omelette on a large serving plate and top with half the couscous. Put another omelette on top, then the rest of the couscous and the last omelette. Top with the tomato and fennel salad. Cut into four wedges to serve.

Serves 4

Nutrition per serve: Energy: 1086 kJ (259 Cals); Protein: 15 g; Total fat: 3 g; Carbohydrate: 41 g; Fibre: 4 g; Sodium: 223 mg

poached sea bass with coriander and sesame crumb and mango salsa

4 x 125 g (4½ oz) pieces sea bass

2 tablespoons lemon juice

50 g (1¾ oz) snow peas, blanched and julienned

crumb

3 tablespoons toasted sesame seeds

3 tablespoons shredded coconut

3 tablespoons chopped fresh coriander (cilantro)

zest and juice of 1 lime

1 teaspoon maple syrup

salsa

1 mango, finely diced

1 small red onion, finely diced

1 red capsicum (pepper), finely diced

2 tablespoons chopped fresh coriander (cilantro) leaves

zest and juice of 1 lime

1 teaspoon fish sauce

½ teaspoon golden door chilli (page 180)

Preheat the oven to 200°C (400°F/Gas 6). Put the fish on a paper-lined baking tray, sprinkle with salt and pepper and drizzle with the lemon juice and 2 tablespoons of water.

Put the crumb ingredients in a food processor and mix until well combined. Spread over the top of the fish. Poach in the oven for about 10 minutes or until the fish is cooked through.

To make the salsa, mix together all the ingredients, season with salt and pepper and leave for a few minutes before serving with the fish. Garnish with snow peas.

Serves 4

CHEF'S TIP: This is delicious served with sweet potato mash (page 112).

Nutrition per serve: Energy: 1032 kJ (246 Cals); Protein: 29 g; Total fat: 10 g; Carbohydrate: 11 g; Fibre: 3 g; Sodium: 258 mg

cinnamon waffles with orange and apple compôte

orange and apple compôte

2 apples

1 teaspoon orange zest

1 teaspoon orange juice

1 teaspoon apple juice concentrate

1 teaspoon apple balsamic vinegar

60 g (2¼ oz) wholemeal flour

60 g (2¼ oz) plain (all-purpose) flour

¼ teaspoon ground cinnamon

½ teaspoon baking powder

pinch of salt

2 teaspoons icing (confectioners') sugar

1 egg, separated, and 2 egg whites

250 ml (9 fl oz/1 cup) skim milk

1 teaspoon grapeseed oil

To make the orange and apple compôte, peel the apples and cut them into matchsticks. Put them in a small pan with the orange zest and juice, apple concentrate and vinegar. Cook for about 10 minutes, stirring frequently to prevent sticking.

Sift together the flours, cinnamon, baking powder, salt and sugar. Beat the egg yolk with the milk and oil. Pour into the flour mixture and stir together just enough to moisten the dry ingredients. Beat the 3 egg whites until stiff peaks form and then fold into the mixture.

Heat a waffle maker and spray lightly with oil. Use about 125 ml (4 fl oz/½ cup) of batter for each waffle. Cook the waffles for about 4–5 minutes and serve with the orange and apple compôte.

Serves 4

CHEF'S TIP: Apple balsamic vinegar is available from speciality food stores. If you can't find it, use ordinary balsamic vinegar instead.

Nutrition per serve: Energy: 846 kJ (202 Cals); Protein: 9 g; Total fat: 3 g; Carbohydrate: 34 g; Fibre: 4 g; Sodium: 180 mg

orange and raspberry cheesecake with mango coulis

1 kg (2 lb 4 oz) low-fat cottage cheese

3 eggs, plus 2 egg whites

juice and zest of 1 lemon

juice and zest of 1 orange

4 tablespoons cornflour (cornstarch)

125 g (4½ oz/½ cup) honey

90 g (3¼ oz/1 cup) cooked rice flakes, crushed

300 g (10½ oz) raspberries

mango coulis (page 187), to serve

Preheat the oven to 140°C (275°F/Gas 1). Put the cottage cheese, eggs and egg whites, lemon juice and zest, orange juice and zest, cornflour and honey in a food processor and mix until smooth.

Lightly crush the rice flakes and spread them on a paper-lined 30 x 25 cm (12 x 10 inch) baking tray. Pour the cheese mixture over the rice flakes and top with half the raspberries. Bake for 45 minutes or until set and golden.

Allow to cool, then chill in the fridge and serve with mango coulis (about 1 tablespoon per person) and the remaining raspberries.

Serves 12

Nutrition per serve: Energy: 820 kJ (196 Cals); Protein: 18 g; Total fat: 3 g; Carbohydrate: 25 g; Fibre: 2 g; Sodium: 144 mg

pan-fried bananas with pineapple ice cream

250 g (9 oz/1 cup) low-fat yoghurt

juice of 1 pineapple (or 250 ml/9 fl oz/ 1 cup pineapple juice)

½ egg white

3 tablespoons apple juice concentrate

250 ml (9 fl oz/1 cup) reduced-fat coconut milk

3 bananas

1 teaspoon grapeseed oil

Put the yoghurt, pineapple juice, egg white, apple concentrate, coconut milk and one of the bananas in a blender and mix for 30 seconds. Transfer to an ice cream machine and leave for 20 minutes until set.

Slice the other two bananas lengthways. Lightly oil a non-stick frying pan with grapeseed oil and cook the banans for 1–2 minutes on each side until soft.

Serve the bananas with a scoop of pineapple ice cream.

Serves 4

Nutrition per serve: Energy: 629 kJ (150 Cals); Protein: 4 g; Total fat: 5 g; Carbohydrate: 21 g; Fibre: 0 g; Sodium: 72 mg

mint and pineapple salad with orange and ginger sorbet

7.5 cm (3 inch) piece of fresh ginger

zest and juice of 1 orange

40 g (1½ oz) palm sugar (jaggery), chopped

1 teaspoon finely chopped pickled ginger

3 teaspoons apple juice concentrate

½ egg white

1 kg (2 lb 4 oz) pineapple, peeled, cored and finely diced

1 tablespoon shredded fresh mint

Grate the fresh ginger and squeeze it until you have 1 tablespoon of juice. Put the ginger juice, orange zest and juice, palm sugar, picked ginger and 2 teaspoons of apple concentrate in a pan and boil gently for 5 minutes.

Add the egg white and transfer to an ice cream machine for 15 minutes.

Mix together the pineapple, mint and remaining apple concentrate and leave to marinate for 30 minutes. Serve with a scoop of the sorbet.

Serves 4

Nutrition per serve: Energy: 400 kJ (96 Cals); Protein: 2 g; Total fat: 0 g; Carbohydrate: 22 g; Fibre: 2 g; Sodium: 13 mg

passionfruit sorbet with toasted melon

juice from 4 passionfruit

50 g (1¾ oz) palm sugar (jaggery), chopped

3 tablespoons apple juice concentrate

½ egg white

12 small cubes of watermelon

12 small cubes of honeydew melon

icing (confectioners') sugar, to sprinkle

Mix together the passionfruit juice, palm sugar, apple concentrate and egg white in a pan. Warm gently over low heat to dissolve the sugar, then cool in the fridge. Transfer to an ice cream machine for 15 minutes until firm.

Preheat the oven to 160°C (310°F/Gas 2–3). Thread the melon cubes alternately onto four skewers. Sprinkle with the sieved icing sugar and roast for 7 minutes, until the melon has caramelized. Serve immediately with the sorbet.

Serves 4

Nutrition per serve: Energy: 445 kJ (106 cal); Protein: 1 g; Total fat: 0 g; Carbohydrate: 26 g; Fibre: 3 g; Sodium: 29 mg

coconut and apricot sorbet with blueberry crush

30 g (1 oz) dried apricots

juice of 2 apples (about 125 ml/4 fl oz/½ cup)

1 teaspoon raw sugar

2 teaspoons apple juice concentrate

250 ml (9 fl oz/1 cup) reduced-fat coconut milk

1 teaspoon coconut powder

½ egg white

12 blueberries, chopped

blueberry crush

50 g (1¾ oz) blueberries

1 teaspoon icing (confectioners') sugar

Put the apricots, apple juice, raw sugar and apple concentrate in a pan and bring to the boil. Reduce the heat and simmer for 15 minutes, until the apricots are very soft. Transfer to a blender and mix to a purée. Cool.

Mix together the coconut milk, coconut powder, egg white, blueberries and apricot purée. Chill in the fridge and then put in an ice cream machine for 15 minutes. Transfer to a small terrine mould and leave in the freezer until set.

To make the blueberry crush, mash the blueberries and icing sugar together with a fork. Remove the terrine from the mould, slice and serve with the blueberry crush on the side.

Serves 4

Nutrition per serve: Energy: 397 kJ (95 Cals); Protein: 1 g; Total fat: 4 g; Carbohydrate: 13 g; Fibre: 1 g; Sodium: 25 mg

saffron vanilla custard

250 ml (9 fl oz/1 cup) skim milk
½ vanilla bean
1 teaspoon cornflour (cornstarch)
3 egg yolks
10 saffron threads
3 teaspoons caster (superfine) sugar
3 teaspoons apple juice concentrate

Put the milk in a pan with the vanilla and bring slowly to boiling point. Remove from the heat and leave to infuse. In a large bowl, mix the cornflour with 2 tablespoons of water until smooth. Add the egg yolks, saffron, sugar and apple concentrate. Whisk in the milk, then tip back into the pan. Bring back to boiling point, stirring constantly, then reduce the heat and simmer for 5 minutes, until thick enough to coat the back of a spoon.

Serves 4

Nutrition per serve: Energy: 358 kJ (86 Cals); Protein: 4 g; Total fat: 4 g; Carbohydrate: 9 g; Fibre: 0 g; Sodium: 38 mg

berry ricotta cakes with honey pistachio yoghurt

12 won ton wrappers

60 g (2¼ oz) low-fat ricotta cheese

60 g (2¼ oz) low-fat cottage cheese

2 teaspoons sugar

1 egg, lightly beaten, and 1 egg yolk

zest of ½ lemon

8 strawberries

2 teaspoons cornflour (cornstarch)

3 teaspoons poppy seeds

3 teaspoons sesame seeds

1 teaspoon honey

2 teaspoons crushed toasted pistachio nuts

125 g (4½ oz/½ cup) low-fat yoghurt

Preheat the oven to 160 C (310°F/Gas 2–3). Line twelve 125 ml (4 fl oz/½ cup) muffin tins with the wrappers and blind bake for 10 minutes until lightly golden.

Put the cheeses, sugar, egg, egg yolk, lemon zest, berries and cornflour in a blender and mix until smooth. Spoon into the baked wrappers and bake for 10 minutes. Sprinkle heavily with the seeds and bake for another 2–3 minutes.

Stir together the honey, pistachio nuts and yoghurt and serve with the cakes.

Serves 4

CHEF'S TIP: You can use other berries that are in season.

Nutrition per serve: Energy: 878 kJ (210 Cals); Protein: 13 g; Total fat: 7 g; Carbohydrate: 24 g; Fibre: 2 g; Sodium: 277 mg

almond and fig torte
with tropical coulis

175 g (6 oz/1 cup) dried apricots

175 g (6 oz/1 cup) dried dates

85 g (3 oz/½ cup) shelled whole almonds

160 g (5¾ oz/1 cup) dried figs

1 teaspoon orange zest

2 teaspoons orange juice

3 tablespoons carob powder

2 litres (70 fl oz/8 cups) low-fat sorbet or ice cream (use 2 different flavours), slightly softened

225 g (8 oz) frozen blueberries or raspberries

mango or berry coulis (page 187), to serve

Put the apricots, dates, almonds and figs in a food processor in batches and process into rough crumbs. Add the orange zest, juice and carob and blend for another minute.

Spread the mixture onto a large sheet of baking paper and cover with another sheet of baking paper. With a rolling pin, roll the mixture to a thickness of 2 mm (¹⁄₁₆ inch). Remove the top sheet of paper and cut two discs to fit a 26 cm (10½ inch) springform tin.

Line the base of the tin with baking paper. This dessert is made upside-down in the tin. Put the frozen berries in the tin, then spoon half the sorbet or ice cream over the top. Put one of the dried fruit discs over the top and freeze for 1 hour to firm the sorbet.

Spoon the rest of the sorbet over the top, then place the other dried fruit disc on top and freeze for 4 hours. Turn out of the springform tin onto a plate and serve with mango or berry coulis.

Serves 14

Nutrition per serve: Energy: 906 kJ (216 Cals); Protein: 6 g; Total fat: 6 g; Carbohydrate: 35 g; Fibre: 4 g; Sodium: 66 mg

fruit ice creams

strawberry and banana ice cream

500 g (1 lb 2 oz) strawberries

500 g (1 lb 2 oz) ripe bananas

banana and custard apple ice cream

500 g (1 lb 2 oz) ripe bananas

500 g (1 lb 2 oz) custard apple flesh, seeds removed

mango and mint ice cream

1 kg (2 lb 4 oz) ripe mango, peeled

3 tablespoons chopped fresh mint

Whichever type of ice cream you are making, thinly slice your fruit and put it on a paper-lined baking tray. Leave in the freezer until half frozen.

Put the fruit in a food processor and blend until thick and creamy. Transfer to an airtight container, put back in the freezer for 1 hour and then serve.

If left overnight, the ice cream will become very hard. Remove from the freezer, thaw slightly and then blend again in the food processor.

Each makes about 1.5 litres (52 fl oz/6 cups)

Nutrition per 250 ml (9 fl oz/1 cup) strawberry and banana:
Energy: 491 kJ (117 Cals); Protein: 3 g; Total fat: 0 g;
Carbohydrate: 26 g; Fibre: 4 g; Sodium: 6 mg

Nutrition per 250 ml (9 fl oz/1 cup) banana and custard apple:
Energy: 817 kJ (195 Cals); Protein: 4 g; Total fat: 0 g;
Carbohydrate: 44 g; Fibre: 6 g; Sodium: 5 mg

Nutrition per 250 ml (9 fl oz/1 cup) mango and mint:
Energy: 414 kJ (99 Cals); Protein: 2 g; Total fat: 0 g;
Carbohydrate: 22g; Fibre: 3 g; Sodium: 2 mg

almond angel cakes with baked figs

100 g (3½ oz/1 cup) ground almonds
110 g (3¾ oz/½ cup) caster (superfine) sugar
50 g (1¾ oz/½ cup) skim milk powder
80 g (2¾ oz/½ cup) desiccated coconut
zest of 1 lemon
6 fresh figs
3 egg whites

Preheat the oven to 160°C (315°F/Gas 2–3). Mix together the ground almonds, sugar, milk powder, coconut and lemon zest. Dice two of the figs and add to the mixture.

Beat the egg whites until soft peaks form and fold into the mixture. Spoon the mixture into ten 125 ml (4 fl oz/½ cup) lightly oiled muffin tins. Bake for 15 minutes and then remove from the oven to cool a little.

Turn up the oven to 180°C (350°F/Gas 4). Cut the remaining figs in half, put on a baking tray and roast in the oven for 10 minutes. Serve each cake with half a baked fig on the side.

Serves 8

CHEF'S TIP: The leftover cakes can be stored in an airtight container for up to 2 days.

Nutrition per serve: Energy: 968 kJ (231 Cals); Protein: 7 g; Total fat: 14 g; Carbohydrate: 21 g; Fibre: 5 g; Sodium: 51 mg

basics

basics

Taste is the main reason why people choose to eat the foods they do and sometimes a plain grilled fish or salad needs something to give it that extra flavour boost. You can enjoy our sauces and dressings in the knowledge that they are created with both taste and nutrition in mind. Commercial stock, sauces and condiments often come loaded with fat and sodium, so our chefs have created some nutritious, low-fat alternatives that are truly delicious.

One of our chefs' favourites is a basic but miraculous white sauce that is low in saturated fat and packed with the goodness of cashew nuts. Cashews contain phytosterols; a substance that can actually lower blood cholesterol. This versatile sauce is the building block for a number of our main meals, freeing you to cook lasagne or fettucine carbonara without compromising on nutrition.

The healthy alternatives to spreading butter on your bread are our baba ganoush, hummus and guacamole. All of these are quick and easy to make and will keep well for a few days in an airtight container in the fridge. And our fruit coulis are a simple and clever way to enjoy a sweet treat.

fresh vitality pure nourishing luscious healthy balance variety fresh vitality pure nourishing luscious healthy balance variety

vegetable stock

3 corn cobs

1 small pumpkin (squash), peeled, seeded and chopped

2 onions

1 teaspoon sea salt

Remove the husks from the corn and cut the cobs in half. Put in a large saucepan with the pumpkin, onions, salt and 4 litres (140 fl oz/16 cups) of water and bring to the boil.

Reduce the heat, cover the pan and leave to simmer for 30 minutes. Strain through a fine sieve and allow to cool. Skim the surface before using.

Makes 4 litres (140 fl oz/16 cups)

CHEF'S TIP: After straining, cut the kernels from the corn cobs and use in salads and soups. The stock can be kept in the fridge for 2–3 days or the freezer for up to 4 months.

Nutrition per 250 ml (9 fl oz/1 cup): Energy: 0 kJ (0 Cals); Protein: 0 g; Total fat: 0 g; Carbohydrate: 0 g; Fibre: 0 g; Sodium: 154 mg

dashi stock

1 kombu stick

6 g (⅛ oz) bonito flakes

Bring 1.25 litres (44 fl oz/5 cups) of water to the boil and then remove from the heat. Add the kombu and bonito flakes and leave for 30 minutes to let the flavours develop. Drain the stock through a fine sieve before using.

Makes 1.25 litres (44 fl oz/5 cups)

Nutrition per 250 ml (9 fl oz/1 cup): Energy: 0 kJ (0 Cals); Protein: 0 g; Total fat: 0 g; Carbohydrate: 0 g; Fibre: 0 g; Sodium: 52 mg

fish stock

300 g (10½ oz) fish bones and offcuts
1 leek, chopped
4 sprigs fresh dill
1 corn cob
4 sprigs fresh parsley
1 fennel bulb

Put all the ingredients in a large saucepan with 3 litres (104 fl oz/12 cups) of water and bring to the boil. Reduce the heat, cover the pan and leave to simmer for 20 minutes. Strain through a fine sieve and allow to cool. Skim the surface before using.

Makes 3 litres (104 fl oz/12 cups)

CHEF'S TIP: This can be kept in the fridge for 2–3 days or the freezer for up to 4 months.

Nutrition per 250 ml (9 fl oz/1 cup): Energy: 0 kJ (0 Cals); Protein: 0 g; Total fat: 0 g; Carbohydrate: 0 g; Fibre: 0 g; Sodium: 30 mg

citrus vinaigrette

zest of 1 lemon
juice of 5 lemons
juice and zest of ½ orange
juice and zest of 1 lime
2 teaspoons sweet chilli sauce
2 small red chillies
1 tablespoon grated palm sugar (jaggery)
2 tablespoons rice vinegar
1 teaspoon chopped fresh mint

Put all the ingredients in a blender and mix until smooth. Add a little water if you prefer a milder flavour. Serve with salad leaves.

Makes 250 ml (9 fl oz/1 cup)

Nutrition per 1 tablespoon: Energy: 166 kJ (40 Cals); Protein: 1 g; Total fat: 0 g; Carbohydrate: 7 g; Fibre: 0 g; Sodium: 5 mg

avocado dressing

1 avocado
3 tablespoons lemon juice
2 garlic cloves

Put all the ingredients in a blender with 375 ml (13 fl oz/ 1½ cups) of water and season to taste. Mix until smooth. Keep in an airtight jar in the fridge for up to 3 weeks.

Makes 500 ml (17 fl oz/2 cups)

Nutrition per 1 tablespoon: Energy: 89 kJ (21 Cals); Protein: 0 g; Total fat: 2 g; Carbohydrate: 0 g; Fibre: 0 g; Sodium: 0 mg

cucumber, yoghurt and mint dressing

1 lemon
½ telegraph cucumber, seeded and finely chopped
250 g (9 oz/1 cup) low-fat yoghurt
2 teaspoons chopped fresh mint

Zest the lemon and then cut in half and juice one half. Put the zest and juice in a blender with the remaining ingredients and mix until smooth. Season to taste. Keep in an airtight jar in the fridge.

Makes 500 ml (17 fl oz/2 cups)

Nutrition per 1 tablespoon: Energy: 45 kJ (11 Cals); Protein: 1 g; Total fat: 0 g; Carbohydrate: 1 g; Fibre: 0 g; Sodium: 14 mg

spicy balsamic dressing

3 tablespoons balsamic vinegar
4 tablespoons lemon juice
1 tablespoon maple syrup
¼ teaspoon golden door chilli
(page 180)

Mix together all the ingredients and season to taste.

Makes 170 ml (5½ fl oz/⅔ cup)

Nutrition per 1 tablespoon: Energy: 53 kJ (13 Cals); Protein: 0 g;
Total fat: 0 g; Carbohydrate: 3 g; Fibre: 0 g; Sodium: 2 mg

pickled ginger dressing

3 cm (1 inch) piece of fresh ginger
60 g (2 oz) pickled ginger, drained
75 ml (2½ oz) verjuice
25 ml (1 fl oz) grapeseed oil
25 ml (1 fl oz) sweet chilli sauce

Grate the fresh ginger and squeeze out the juice (discard
the pulp). Mix the juice with the remaining ingredients in a
blender until smooth. Keep in an airtight jar in the fridge.

Makes 170 ml (5½ fl oz/⅔ cup)

Nutrition per 1 tablespoon: Energy: 135 kJ (32 Cals); Protein: 0 g;
Total fat: 2 g; Carbohydrate: 3 g; Fibre: 0 g; Sodium: 2 mg

grapefruit and mango dressing

juice and zest of ½ grapefruit

½ teaspoon cornflour (cornstarch)

½ mango, mashed

2 tablespoons apple juice concentrate

2 teaspoons white balsamic vinegar

juice and zest of 1 lime

¼ teaspoon celery salt

ground black pepper, to taste

Put the grapefruit juice in a pan with 125 ml (4 fl oz/ ½ cup) of water and bring to the boil. Mix the cornflour with 2 teaspoons of water until smooth, then add to the pan. Stir until smooth then cool. Transfer to a blender, add the remaining ingredients and blend until smooth.

Makes 375 ml (13 fl oz/1½ cups)

Nutrition per 1 tablespoon: Energy: 65 kJ (16 Cals); Protein: 0 g; Total fat: 0 g; Carbohydrate: 4 g; Fibre: 0 g; Sodium: 5 mg

wasabi lime dressing

2 teaspoons tamari soy sauce

1 teaspoon lime zest

1 tablespoon lime juice

1 teaspoon lemon zest

1 tablespoon lemon juice

1 teaspoon sesame oil

1–2 teaspoons wasabi, to taste

1 teaspoon toasted sesame seeds

Whisk together all the ingredients.

Makes 4 tablespoons

CHEF'S TIP: This dressing is delicious with a few drops of Boyajian lime oil added (available at speciality food shops).

Nutrition per 1 tablespoon: Energy: 79 kJ (19 Cals); Protein: 0 g; Total fat: 2 g; Carbohydrate: 1 g; Fibre: 0 g; Sodium: 12 mg

roasted capsicum and dijon dressing

1 red capsicum (pepper), roasted (page 113)

1 tomato, roasted (page 113)

1 garlic clove, roasted (page 113)

1 teaspoon balsamic vinegar

1 teaspoon sugar

2 teaspoons dijon mustard

1 teaspoon sweet chilli sauce

2 teaspoons pumpkin oil

Peel the roasted capsicum, tomato and garlic and place in a blender with the remaining ingredients. Mix until smooth and add salt and pepper to taste.

Makes 150 ml (5 fl oz)

Nutrition per 1 tablespoon: Energy: 87 kJ (21 Cals); Protein: 1 g; Total fat: 0 g; Carbohydrate: 2 g; Fibre: 1 g; Sodium: 12 mg

eggplant and cinnamon dressing

1 eggplant (aubergine)

1 teaspoon apple juice concentrate

½ teaspoon ground cinnamon

1 teaspoon virgin olive oil

1 teaspoon tamarind paste

2 teaspoons white balsamic vinegar

Preheat the oven to 180°C (350°F/Gas 4). Prick the eggplant all over with a fork, wrap loosely in foil and roast for 1 hour. Cool and then scrape off the skin. Place in a blender with the remaining ingredients and blend until smooth. Season to taste and add a little water to thin the dressing if necessary.

Makes 250 ml (9 fl oz/1 cup)

Nutrition per 1 tablespoon: Energy: 34 kJ (8 Cals); Protein: 0 g; Total fat: 0 g; Carbohydrate: 1 g; Fibre: 0 g; Sodium: 1 mg

mustard yoghurt dressing

125 ml (4 fl oz/½ cup) wholegrain
mustard

250 g (9 oz/1 cup) low-fat yoghurt

juice and rind of 1 lemon

2 teaspoons chopped fresh mint

2 teaspoons chopped fresh coriander
(cilantro)

Put all the ingredients in a blender with 2 tablespoons of
water and mix until smooth.

Makes 375 ml (13 fl oz/1½ cups)

Nutrition per 1 tablespoon: Energy: 53 kJ (13 Cals); Protein: 0 g;
Total fat: 0 g; Carbohydrate: 3 g; Fibre: 0 g; Sodium: 2 mg

roasted macadamia and shallot dressing

4 French shallots, peeled

2 teaspoons balsamic vinegar

1 teaspoon honey

80 g (2¾ oz/½ cup) roasted macadamia
nuts

2 teaspoons tamari soy sauce

1 teaspoon tamarind paste

½ teaspoon tahini

1 teaspoon English mustard

¼ teaspoon mustard seed oil

Preheat the oven to 160°C (315°F/Gas 2–3). Wrap the
shallots and vinegar in foil and roast on a baking tray for
1 hour until soft. Transfer to a blender, add the remaining
ingredients and blend until smooth. Season to taste and
thin with a little water if necessary.

Makes 200 ml (7 fl oz)

Nutrition per 1 tablespoon: Energy: 239 kJ (57 Cals); Protein: 1 g;
Total fat: 6 g; Carbohydrate: 1 g; Fibre: 1 g; Sodium: 44 mg

dukka

25 g (1 oz) hazelnuts
25 g (1 oz) whole almonds
3 tablespoons sumac
3 teaspoons celery salt
2 tablespoons dried thyme leaves
2 teaspoons garlic powder
1 tablespoon smoked paprika
4 teaspoons ground black pepper
3 teaspoons ground coriander
75 g (2½ oz) roasted chickpeas

Preheat the oven to 180°C (350°F/Gas 4). Put the nuts on a baking tray and roast for 7–10 minutes. Put the spices on a paper-lined baking tray and roast for 20 minutes, stirring frequently, until aromatic. Leave to cool, then finely chop the nuts, spices and chickpeas in a blender. Store in an airtight container and use to coat meat and chicken.

Makes 225 g (8 oz/1½ cups)

Nutrition per 1 tablespoon: Energy: 90 kJ (21 Cals); Protein: 1 g; Total fat: 2 g; Carbohydrate: 1 g; Fibre: 0 g; Sodium: 131 mg

tomato pasta sauce

2 teaspoons olive oil
1 small onion, diced
1 garlic clove, crushed
pinch of paprika
1 tablespoon tomato paste (purée)
500 g (1 lb 2 oz/2 cups) canned tomatoes
4 small tomatoes, diced
2 teaspoons sweet chilli sauce
pinch of celery salt
pinch of pepper
1 teaspoon cornflour (cornstarch)
1 teaspoon balsamic vinegar
1 teaspoon chopped fresh basil

Heat the oil and fry the onion over low heat for 2 minutes. Add the garlic, cook for 1 minute, then add the paprika, tomato paste and canned tomatoes. Cook for 10 minutes.

Add 250 ml (9 fl oz/1 cup) of water and bring to the boil. Boil for 5 minutes, then add the diced tomatoes, sweet chilli sauce, celery salt and pepper and bring back to the boil for 2–3 minutes. Mix the cornflour with 2 tablespoons of water until smooth and add to the pan with the vinegar. Bring back to the boil for 2 minutes, then stir in the basil.

Makes about 1 litre (35 fl oz/4 cups)

Nutrition per 250 ml (9 fl oz/1 cup): Energy: 263 kJ (63 Cals); Protein: 2 g; Total fat: 2 g; Carbohydrate: 8 g; Fibre: 3 g; Sodium: 120 mg

white sauce

500 g (1 lb 2 oz) leeks, white part only, chopped
50 g (1¾ oz) cashew nuts
400 ml (14 fl oz) low-fat soy milk
1½ teaspoons cornflour (cornstarch)

Sauté the leeks and cashew nuts in a little water until soft. Transfer to a blender and add the milk. Blend until smooth and then return to the pan.

Mix the cornflour with 2 teaspoons of water until smooth, and then add to the sauce. Bring back to the boil. If the sauce seems too thick, add more milk. If too thin, add more cornflour. Season with salt and pepper.

This sauce is ideal for lasagne, dressing vegetables or for adding to potatoes before mashing.

Makes 750 ml (26 fl oz/3 cups)

Nutrition per 250 ml (9 fl oz/1 cup): Energy: 855 kJ (204 Cals); Protein: 11 g; Total fat: 10 g; Carbohydrate: 19 g; Fibre: 7 g; Sodium: 86 mg

golden door chilli

300 g (10½ oz) chillies
2 tablespoons apple cider
2 tablespoons tamari soy sauce

Put all the ingredients in food processor and blend thoroughly. Store in an airtight container in the fridge.

Makes 375 ml (13 fl oz/1½ cups)

Nutrition per 1 tablespoon: Energy: 23 kJ (5 Cals); Protein: 0 g; Total fat: 0 g; Carbohydrate: 1 g; Fibre: 0 g; Sodium: 78 mg

low-fat dijon mayonnaise

300 g (10½ oz) silken tofu
185 ml (6 fl oz/¾ cup) dijon mustard
185 ml (6 fl oz/¾ cup) lemon juice
4 tablespoons apple juice concentrate
1 garlic clove, roasted (page 113)

Put all the ingredients in a blender, mix until smooth and season to taste. The mayonnaise will keep for up to 2 weeks in an airtight container in the fridge.

Makes 750 ml (26 fl oz/3 cups)

Nutrition per 1 tablespoon: Energy: 656 kJ (15 Cals); Protein: 1 g; Total fat: 1 g; Carbohydrate: 2 g; Fibre: 0 g; Sodium: 78 mg

red capsicum sauce

1 large red capsicum (pepper), chopped into large pieces
2 teaspoons apple cider vinegar
2 tablespoons apple juice concentrate
1 teaspoon paprika
¼ teaspoon sea salt
1 garlic clove, roasted (page 113)

Put the capsicum in a saucepan and cover with water. Bring to the boil, reduce the heat and simmer for 10 minutes or until the capsicum is soft.

Drain and put the capsicum in a blender with all the other ingredients. Blend until smooth. Pass the sauce through a fine sieve to remove any capsicum skin. Keep in an airtight container in the fridge and serve cold or warmed.

Makes 375 ml (13 fl oz/1½ cups)

Nutrition per 1 tablespoon: Energy: 28 kJ (7 Cals); Protein: 0 g; Total fat: 0 g; Carbohydrate: 2 g; Fibre: 0 g; Sodium: 34 mg

mango salsa

1 mango, diced

½ red capsicum (pepper), roasted, peeled and diced (page 113)

1 small red onion, diced

1 tablespoon orange juice

2 teaspoons finely chopped fresh mint

2 teaspoons finely chopped fresh coriander (cilantro)

Gently fold together all the ingredients in a bowl and season to taste. Cover and leave for 1 hour for the flavours to develop. Serve with steamed fish or poached chicken.

Makes 280 g (10 oz/1½ cups)

Nutrition per 1 tablespoon: Energy: 35 kJ (8 Cals); Protein: 0 g; Total fat: 0 g; Carbohydrate: 2 g; Fibre: 0 g; Sodium: 1 mg

hummus

220 g (7¾ oz/1 cup) chickpeas, soaked overnight, rinsed and boiled until soft

125 ml (4 fl oz/½ cup) golden door yoghurt (page 34)

1 tablespoon cumin

2–3 tablespoons lemon juice

1 tablespoon tahini

½ teaspoon paprika

1 garlic clove, roasted (page 113)

1 teaspoon sea salt

pinch of ground black pepper

Put all the ingredients in a food processor and blend until smooth. Keep in an airtight container in the fridge.

CHEF'S TIP: For smooth hummus, use warm chickpeas.

Makes 750 ml (26 fl oz/3 cups)

Nutrition per 1 tablespoon: Energy: 71 kJ (17 Cals); Protein: 1 g; Total fat: 1 g; Carbohydrate: 2 g; Fibre: 1 g; Sodium: 68 mg

mango salsa

baba ganoush

1 large eggplant (aubergine), approximately 1 kg (2 lb 4 oz)

1 garlic clove, roasted (page 113)

125 ml (4 fl oz/½ cup) golden door yoghurt (page 34)

3 tablespoons lemon juice

2 teaspoons cumin

¼ teaspoon salt

¼ teaspoon pepper

¼ teaspoon paprika

1½ tablespoons tahini

Preheat the oven to 200°C (400°F/Gas 6). Cut the eggplant lengthways into quarters and put on a paper-lined baking tray. Bake for about 20 minutes or until tender. Cool and then remove the skin.

Put the eggplant in a food processor and add the remaining ingredients. Process until smooth, adding a little hot water until you have a good consistency.

Makes 750 ml (26 fl oz/3 cups)

Nutrition per 1 tablespoon: Energy: 49 kJ (12 Cals); Protein: 1 g; Total fat: 1 g; Carbohydrate: 1 g; Fibre: 1 g; Sodium: 21 mg

guacamole

2 avocados

2 tablespoons lemon juice

2 cloves garlic, roasted (page 113)

2 tablespoons golden door yoghurt (page 34)

¼ teaspoon cumin powder

pinch each of cayenne pepper, sea salt and black pepper

2 teaspoons snipped chives

2 teaspoons chopped coriander (cilantro)

Mash the avocados roughly with a fork. Add the lemon juice, garlic, yoghurt, cumin and seasoning and mash together. Fold in the chives and coriander and serve immediately.

Makes 500 ml (17 fl oz/2 cups)

Nutrition per 1 tablespoon: Energy: 187 kJ (45 Cals); Protein: 1 g; Total fat: 4 g; Carbohydrate: 1 g; Fibre: 0 g; Sodium: 14 mg

balinese satay sauce

1 small onion, diced

1 teaspoon Thai spice powder

3 tablespoons chopped fresh coriander (cilantro) leaves and stems

2 tablespoons peanut butter

1 tablespoon grated fresh ginger

1 garlic clove, roasted (page 113)

3 makrut (kaffir lime) leaves, chopped

3 tablespoons tamari soy sauce

½ teaspoon cornflour (cornstarch)

Put a little water in a pan and sauté the onion, Thai spice and coriander until fragrant and soft.

Put the peanut butter, ginger, garlic, lime leaves, tamari, cornflour and 325 ml (11 fl oz) of water in a blender and mix until smooth. Add the onion mix and blend together until smooth. Pour the sauce back into the pan and bring to the boil over low heat, whisking continuously. Keep in an airtight container in the fridge for up to 1 week. Serve with chicken, fish or vegetables, or as part of gado gado.

Makes 375 ml (13 fl oz/1½ cups)

Nutrition per 1 tablespoon: Energy: 82 kJ (20 Cals); Protein: 1 g; Total fat: 1 g; Carbohydrate: 1 g; Fibre: 0 g; Sodium: 118 mg

spinach and avocado coulis

125 g (4½ oz/2 cups) English spinach

1 avocado

3 tablespoons lemon juice

3 tablespoons apple juice concentrate

4 sprigs fresh mint

1 garlic clove, roasted (page 113)

¼ teaspoon trocomare (herb salt)

½ teaspoon sea salt

pinch of black pepper

Lightly blanch the spinach in boiling water, then run under cold water and wrap in a clean cloth to dry. Put the spinach in a blender with all the other ingredients and 250 ml (9 fl oz/1 cup) of water and process until smooth. Serve with salad or vegetables.

Makes 375 ml (13 fl oz/1½ cups)

Nutrition per 1 tablespoon: Energy: 115 kJ (27 Cals); Protein: 0 g; Total fat: 2 g; Carbohydrate: 2 g; Fibre: 0 g; Sodium: 52 mg

avocado pesto

3 tablespoons pine nuts

150 g (5½ oz/3 cups) fresh basil

4 tablespoons lemon juice

2 garlic cloves, roasted (page 113)

1½ avocados

½ teaspoon trocomare (herb salt)

Put the pine nuts, basil, lemon juice and garlic in a food processor and mix together. Add the remaining ingredients and 125 ml (4 fl oz/½ cup) of water and process until smooth. Add salt and pepper if needed.

Serve with pasta or cooked vegetables. To increase your protein intake, add tuna.

CHEF'S TIP: This will keep for a week in an airtight container in the fridge. If the top discolours, just scrape off a thin layer.

Makes 500 ml (17 fl oz/2 cups)

Nutrition per 1 tablespoon: Energy: 187 kJ (45 Cals); Protein: 1 g; Total fat: 5 g; Carbohydrate: 0 g; Fibre: 0 g; Sodium: 51 mg

sweet chilli sauce

125 ml (4 fl oz/½ cup) apple juice concentrate

1 tablespoon paprika

2 tablespoons tamari soy sauce

1 teaspoon golden door chilli (page 180)

1 garlic clove, crushed (optional)

2 makrut (kaffir lime) leaves (optional)

1 tablespoon cornflour (cornstarch)

Put all the ingredients except the cornflour in a saucepan with 125 ml (4 fl oz/½ cup) of water and bring to the boil.

Mix the cornflour with 2 tablespoons of cold water until smooth, then add to the pan. Bring the sauce back to the boil before serving as a dipping sauce. Keep for up to 4 weeks in an airtight container in the fridge.

Makes 250 ml (9 fl oz/1 cup)

Nutrition per 1 tablespoon: Energy: 112 kJ (27 Cals); Protein: 0 g; Total fat: 0 g; Carbohydrate: 7 g; Fibre: 0 g; Sodium: 7 mg

mango coulis

1 mango, peeled
125 ml (4 fl oz/½ cup) orange juice

Mix the mango and orange juice in a blender until smooth. Serve with your favourite dessert.

Makes 250 ml (9 fl oz/1 cup)

Nutrition per 1 tablespoon: Energy: 53 kJ (13 Cals); Protein: 0 g; Total fat: 0 g; Carbohydrate: 3 g; Fibre: 0 g; Sodium: 1 mg

berry coulis

325 g (11½ oz/1½ cups) berries (try strawberries, blackberries, raspberries)
2 teaspoons maple syrup

Mix the berries and maple syrup in a blender until smooth, then pass through a fine sieve. Serve with your favourite dessert.

CHEF'S TIP: Do not add any liquid to the coulis other than maple syrup as berries have a very high water content. The coulis will tend to separate if water or juice is added.

Makes 375 ml (13 fl oz/1½ cups)

Nutrition per 1 tablespoon: Energy: 25 kJ (6 Cals); Protein: 0 g; Total fat: 0 g; Carbohydrate: 1 g; Fibre: 1 g; Sodium: 0 mg

Published by Murdoch Books Pty Limited

Murdoch Books Pty Limited Australia
Pier 8/9, 23 Hickson Road, Millers Point NSW 2000
Phone + 61 (0) 2 8220 2000 Fax + 61 (0) 2 8220 2558

Murdoch Books UK Limited
Erico House, 6th Floor North, 93–99 Upper Richmond Road, Putney, London SW15 2TG
Phone: + 44 (0) 20 8785 5995   Fax: + 44 (0) 20 8785 5985

Editor: Jane Price
Designer: Susanne Geppert
Photography: Alan Benson; Natasha Milne
Food Styling: Sarah DeNardi
Food Preparation: Julie Ray
Recipe Testing: Michelle Earl, Kathy Knudsen
Photographic Model: Natasha Dillon, Faces

Murdoch Books Chief Executive: Juliet Rogers
Publisher: Kay Scarlett
Editorial Manager: Diana Hill
Production: Monika Paratore
Golden Door Group Product Manager: Carolyn Lange

National Library of Australia Cataloguing-in-Publication Data:
Includes index. ISBN 1 74045 716 1. 1. Cookery. 2. Nutrition. 641.563

Printed in China by C&C Offset Printing Co Ltd.
Reprinted in 2006

THE GOLDEN DOOR HEALTH RETREATS AND SPAS
The Golden Door Health Retreat – Elysia
Thompsons Road, Pokolbin, NSW 2320
Toll Free 1800 212 011 Fax (02) 4993 8599
Email: info@elysia.com.au

The Golden Door Health Retreat – Queensland
400 Ruffles Road, Willow Vale, QLD 4209
Toll Free 1800 816 906 Fax (07) 5546 6173
Email: info@goldendoor.com.au

The Golden Door Spa
Cypress Lakes Resort
Cnr McDonalds and Thompsons Roads, Pokolbin, NSW 2320
Tel (02) 4993 1400 Fax (02) 4993 1499
Email: thegoldendoor@cypresslakes.com.au

The Golden Door Spa and Health Club
Mirage Resort
73 Seaworld Drive, Main Beach, QLD 4217
Tel (07) 5531 3626 Fax (07) 5591 7182
Email: spa&healthclub@goldendoor.com.au

www.goldendoor.com.au